# SERVICES
## on and off the
# Motorways
### Jimmy Young

**David & Charles**
Newton Abbot · London · North Pomfret (Vt)

**British Library Cataloguing in Publication Data**

Young, Jimmy
    Services on and off the motorways.
    1. Restaurants, lunch rooms, etc. –
    Great Britain – Directories
    2. Automobiles – Service Stations –
    Great Britain – Directories
    I. Title
    388.3'12        TX907

    ISBN 0–7153–7609–8

Printed in Great Britain
by Butler and Tanner Limited, Frome
for David & Charles (Publishers) Limited
Brunel House  Newton Abbot  Devon

Published in the United States of America
by David & Charles Inc
North Pomfret  Vermont 05053  USA

# SERVICES
## on and off the
# Motorways

# Contents

Every effort has been made to ensure that the information given is accurate at the time of going to press. Inevitably some changes will occur and the author will be pleased to hear of these, and will be delighted to receive reader's comments and suggestions for items to be included in possible future editions:

Jimmy Young
Red Cross House
Crediton
Devon

# Introduction

The disillusion of the general public with the cost and inefficiency of some motorway service areas has prompted me to write this guide. The criticisms are not common to all, but an overall unsatisfactory impression remains. Few travellers have advance information on where food, accommodation and services are available near Britain's motorways, so I set off, travelling 6274 miles in all, exiting at every major junction on the principal motorways, compiling information on the services available on the motorways, and on the hotels, pubs, cafés, restaurants and garages within three miles of each junction.

## The Role of the Motorway

The term motorway is defined by the Special Roads Act 1957 which lays down standards regarding the gradients, curves, width and alignment of those sections of road that are restricted to certain classes of vehicle.

Motorways were originally designed to link ports and industrial complexes with the larger cities of Britain, and to free many of the A roads from the burden of the ever-increasing heavy-goods vehicles. The safety and efficiency of a motorway could be enhanced by certain improvements; for example, I would like to see:

—the provision of more crawler-lanes on steep gradients
—a noisy road surface added at all intersections as a warning against possible hazards and at regular intervals to awaken the drowsy motorist
—an improvement in visibility at roundabouts, achieved by bringing slip roads further to the side and by tapering railings
—uphill exit-junctions wherever possible to encourage a reduction in speed
—road surfaces covered with an anti-spray material
—the simplification of the arrangements of roads leading to and from motorways instead of the massive and complex roundabouts at some junctions

Many accidents are caused because already existing laws are so often violated. It is forbidden to picnic on the hard-shoulder, hitch-hike on the motorway, or wander up the edge of the motorway in search of petrol, yet these infringements are common. It is an offence to have an insecure load or to throw litter, including cigarette ends, on any highway. A lighted cigarette end thrown out is distracting to following drivers at night and is, of course, a fire risk.

Lorry drivers from abroad are another hazard; probably because they do not understand UK law or because they realise they are protected by their foreign number-plates, they constantly contravene motorway regulations.

Speeding is common. All vehicles are limited to 70 mph, heavy goods vehicles to 60 mph and vehicles towing trailers to 50 mph. These last two categories are not allowed into the third (overtaking) lane and therefore much frustration is caused to lorry drivers by slow driving in the middle (fast) lane as well as to other motorway users.

Where a temporary lower speed limit is imposed (because of poor visibility, accidents, road works, etc) this is often ignored. It might help if gradual speed reductions were imposed over the two or three miles leading to the hazard. At the same time, however, unnecessary restrictions are ultimately dangerous: they lead to a lack of credibility and, therefore, abuse. Hazard signs should be removed immediately work is completed.

Motorway telephones are available only for use in emergencies, as is the hard shoulder. Neither facility should be abused.

Before leaving for a long motorway journey check the condition of your car, the tyre treads and pressures (including the spare), oil, water and the secure fastening of roof-racks and trailers.

**Tolls**  The only motorway toll is on the M4 at the Severn Bridge:

Motor cars 12p } pay at east
Motor cycles 5p } entrance

There are several tolls near motorways. The charges (at time of going to press) are:

| M25 DARTFORD TUNNEL | Motor cars | 25p } pay at south |
| | Motor cycles | 10p } entrance |
| M62 MERSEY TUNNELS | Motor cars | 20p } pay on entry both |
| | Motor cycles | 10p } sides |
| A1(M) TYNE TUNNEL | Motor cars | 15p } pay at north |
| | Motor cycles | 5p } entrance |
| M90 FORTH BRIDGE | Motor cars | 15p pay at south entrance |
| M8 ERSKINE BRIDGE | Motor cars | 15p pay at south entrance |

## Motorway Service Areas

The Ministry of the Environment is ultimately responsible for the siting of the service areas. These are leased out by tender to be developed and run by the top catering companies and large petrol concerns. Each of these companies has to comply with the requirements laid down by the Ministry, including the provision of facilities for the drivers of transport vehicles. Many areas have insufficient parking space to accommodate the quantity of lorries using them at peak times; consequently bottlenecks form at the entrances and spill out onto the motorways causing a serious hazard. A lack of overall design results in considerable wastage of space and prevents the free flow of traffic within the area: more effort could be made to provide for the fluctuations in demand. Complaints that prices at service areas tend to be higher than those in comparable establishments off the motorway are explained by the fact that motorway services have to provide a 24-hour service whereas others can open and close to suit their trade.

**Restaurants** The quality of the restaurants varies considerably from one service area to another, and ranges from moderate to good. One or two service areas provide restaurants where there is a very limited menu and no table service: these I have not considered to be more than cafeterias. It is surprising how few people are using the restaurants where available, despite the fact that a full restaurant breakfast is cheaper than paying piecemeal in a cafeteria. Good quality one-course dishes are available at any time during opening hours, individually cooked, in pleasant surroundings with comfortable seating. Several of the restaurants have been closed because of the lack of public support; this could be remedied by more efficient advertising.

**Cafeterias** The standard of food varies enormously, as do the prices. Generally speaking the quality of cooking is poor; recurrent complaints, to list but a few, are greasy pre-cooked bacon, hard pre-cooked eggs, watery tomatoes and cold soggy chips! Tea and coffee are weak and bread often stale. Features that could be improved upon are the seating, impersonal atmosphere and poorly trained staff. Having said that let me stress that these faults exist only in a few areas. The majority of cafeterias offer a fair service despite being rather strained at times in the summer when large coach parties converge on the service areas.

**Accommodation** A few of the service areas have modern hotels which provide bed and continental or full breakfast in the cafeteria restaurant. These motels all have residential licences. More adequate facilities could be made available to lorry drivers by providing cheap transport rooms within the existing hotels.

**Toilets** Few service areas have sufficient toilets to cope with peak-time demand. I have only once seen a shower and as a rule there are inadequate facilities for lorry drivers who wish to wash and shave and no space for hanging coats, shirts, etc. Standards could be improved if more cleaning staff were employed during peak holiday periods and extra facilities were made available. In the slack periods a toilet block could be locked off, though some toilets must always be available. Several areas provide a special mothers' room which is greatly appreciated.

**Shops** The standard in the shops again varies enormously. Some, particularly those on the tourist routes, mainly stock quick-selling presents leaving the traveller who has forgotten his handkerchief or the mother who has run out of babyfood to look elsewhere.

**Parking** Most areas have insufficient facilities for parking at peak periods. This failing generally applies to those areas allocated to the transport lorries and coaches. In the private-car sections a considerable area is wasted by decorative islands which could be more productively employed as additional parking space.

**Overnight parking** The charge for overnight parking varies, though at the time of this survey it was generally £1 including a 50p voucher for breakfast. As a rule the prices varied between £1 and £1.85, both inclusive of 50p vouchers. A uniform tariff—if a charge is made at all—should be introduced for overnight vehicles parked in the service areas. Consideration should be given by the Department of the Environment to the provision of secure car parks for the drivers of heavy-goods vehicles who are compelled by law to make stops and have rest periods.

**Connecting bridges** Most connecting bridges over motorways are covered and some are used to great advantage as restaurants overlooking the motorway. One area in which the designers have failed is that of providing facilities for invalids to use them. There are loop roads joining one side of the motorway to the other which may be used but have 'no entry' signs displayed to deter constant misuse.

**Lifts** Where buildings are on two levels, a service lift is generally available and clearly marked.

**Garages** Many service areas have franchised out their garage facilities to local firms whilst retaining the petrol and diesel sales themselves. These local firms endeavour to have someone always available to assist the motorist in trouble. Services may be limited to one side of the motorway in which case the connecting road is generally made available.

It is, of course, advisable to be a member of the AA or RAC who will attend to your car free *outside the service area*, making a charge only for parts and towing in excess of an agreed distance. The motorway garages run a considerable risk in providing aid to motorists who not infrequently sign invalid cheques. As a result many garages are sceptical about accepting calls from motorway users. The charges for breakdown services are agreed by the main motor associations and though they may seem high they are fair.

**Fuel** The majority of fuel pumps are now self-service although an attendant is usually available in case of emergency. To my knowledge, only one self-service station on the motorway offers petrol at reduced prices.

**Room for improvement** There are ways in which motorway service areas might be improved in the future. Speeding should be reduced either by placing ramps across the road or adopting the French system of gradually decreasing speed limits placed at intervals along the slip roads from the motorway into the service areas. Poor signing is another hazard that could be improved by better lighting and clearer notices. Other suggestions are as follows:

—the Minister responsible might hold annual meetings with the proprietors of the service areas to iron out the difficulties that arise

—the managers of all service areas might meet quarterly to discuss their individual problems, prices, etc, in a friendly rather than competitive spirit. This could result in mutual benefits to both big and small companies

—several sites that were planned prior to leasing were not taken on by companies; this situation could be avoided if interested companies with knowledge of local requirements were consulted in the design/construction stage.

**The franchised companies** The following is an alphabetical reference list of the companies leasing service areas from the Department of the Environment:

ALAN POUND
Private company
Harthill

BLUE BOAR
Private company
Watford Gap

BLUE STAR
Garage group
Blythe

GRANADA
Television company
Toddington, Heston, Washington Birtley, Frankley, Woolley Edge, Leigh, Southwaite, Birch, Exeter

GRAND METROPOLITAN
Watneys, the brewers
Forth Bridge

KENNING MOTOR GROUP
Westcountry company
Strensham, Anderton

MECCA MOTOR COMPANY
Entertainments concern
Trowell

MERCURY
Motel group
Kennford

| | |
|---|---|
| **MOBIL**<br>Petrol group | Michael Wood, Burton West |
| **MOTOR CHEF**<br>Trust Houses Forte | Scratchwood, Newport Pagnall, Woodall, Fleet, Gordano, Corley, Keele, Charnock, Richard, Burtonwood, Brent Knoll (West) |
| **TOP RANK**<br>Film company which has considerably diversified | Farthing Corner, Aust, Hilton Park, Knutsford, Porton |
| **ROAD CHEF**<br>Galleon group | Hamilton, Bothwell, Sandbach, Rownham, Taunton, Deane, Brent Knoll (East), Killington Lake |
| **ROSS**<br>Frozen food company | Leicester Forest East, Membury, Hartshead Moor |
| **WESTMORLAND**<br>Private company | Trebay |

## Services off the Motorways

**Pubs** Frequently pubs misleadingly refer to themselves as inns, though they provide neither accommodation nor food. The main function of the pub is to serve alcohol, but I have listed under the heading of pubs only those establishments which either serve main-course meals during the major part of the week and snacks at other times, or which offer some kind of accommodation. Several pubs have restaurants that are of a very good standard; (R) after the pub's reference number indicates this.

**Restaurants** *Table d'hôte* (t d'hote) means a set three- or four-course menu, usually with a limited choice, as opposed to *à la carte* (a la c) where one pays individually for each item ordered, and where there is a wide selection. Restaurants may have either a special-hours' certificate or a restaurant licence. The former allows drinks to be served after normal licensing hours, the latter having the same basic principle but with slightly different conditions. First-class hotels are not necessarily prohibitively expensive since most provide a *table d'hôte* menu which gives good value for money if one requires a full meal.

**Cafés** Although they may lack the refinement of established restaurants, the food in cafés is often good, helpings are ample and dishes individually cooked. Some cafés are more like restaurants, but as they do not have a wide menu I have chosen not to include them in the restaurant list. Although cafés cater primarily for the transport drivers, they also appeal to others. Transport drivers are discerning eaters on the road and a good indication of the quality of the food can be gathered from the number of lorries outside cafés.

**Hotels** A number of pubs refer to themselves as hotels although frequently they are unable to provide a sufficient standard of service to merit being listed under this description. It is advisable to enquire in advance what accommodation and services are available.

It is surprising to find that even some purpose-built, modern hotels, sometimes designated as three-star, have no lounge other than the reception foyer. Where a hotel does not have a public licence it is generally referred to as a private hotel. This means that it has a residential licence and only a limited range of alcohol is served, either from a small bar or out of sight at a dispensary.

If overnight accommodation is required it is always advisable to book rooms in advance, particularly if travelling at the weekend or choosing a small hotel. Many larger hotels near cities and towns offer reduced weekend rates.

**Garages** Filling stations frequently change hands, close down, alter their hours, change their brands, etc, so the information given may have changed. Similarly, garages quoted as having prepayment self-service machines may no longer operate them due to vandalism.

# Abbreviations

| | |
|---|---|
| **C** | Café |
| **C(G)** | Café with Garage |
| **G** | Garage |
| **H** | Hotel |
| **H(R)** | Hotel with Restaurant |
| **P** | Pub |
| **P(R)** | Pub with Restaurant |
| **R** | Restaurant |

The author's particular recommendations are surrounded by a box on the following pages

# M1. London-Leeds
## JUNCTIONS 1 – 12

Britain's first Motorway, 73m opened
Nov 1959. Ample petrol & garage
services on North Circular (A406); for
accommodation & meals go to London's
West End or Hampstead. Junction 2
under construction, 3 not planned. M10
is exit spur to St Albans, entry from N
only.

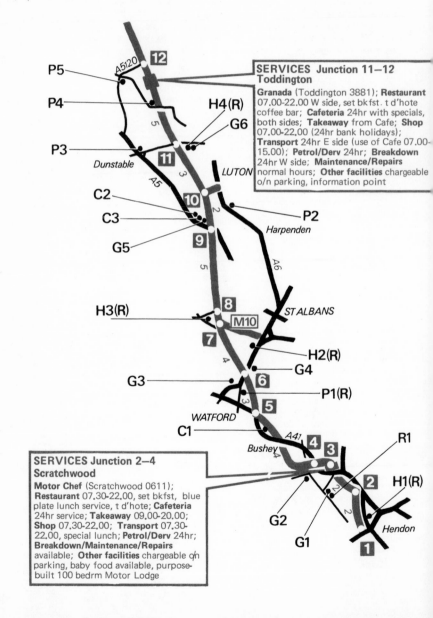

**SERVICES Junction 11–12**
**Toddington**
**Granada** (Toddington 3881); **Restaurant**
07.00-22.00 W side, set bkfst. t d'hote
coffee bar; **Cafeteria** 24hr with specials,
both sides; **Takeaway** from Cafe; **Shop**
07.00-22.00 (24hr bank holidays);
**Transport** 24hr E side (use of Cafe 07.00-
15.00); **Petrol/Derv** 24hr; **Breakdown**
24hr W side; **Maintenance/Repairs**
normal hours; **Other facilities** chargeable
o/n parking, information point

**SERVICES Junction 2–4**
**Scratchwood**
**Motor Chef** (Scratchwood 0611);
**Restaurant** 07.30-22.00, set bkfst, blue
plate lunch service, t d'hote; **Cafeteria**
24hr service; **Takeaway** 09.00-20.00;
**Shop** 07.30-22.00; **Transport** 07.30-
22.00, special lunch; **Petrol/Derv** 24hr;
**Breakdown/Maintenance/Repairs**
available; **Other facilities** chargeable o/n
parking, baby food available, purpose-
built 100 bedrm Motor Lodge

## CAFES

**5**
**C1** Walleys Cafe, Bushey
07.00-19.30 Mon-Fri, meals & snacks, o/n parking
A41 s'posted Bushey ¾m

**9**
**C2** Little Chef, Flamstead
09.00-19.00, grills & light snacks
A5 s'posted Dunstable ¾m

**9**
**C3** Watling Street Transport Cafe, Flamstead
06.00-20.00 Mon-Fri, meals, snacks, B&B
A5 s'posted Dunstable ¼m

## GARAGES

**4**
**G1** Cannons Corner Service Station, Edgware
Shell. 08.00-21.00 (09.00-21.00 Sun)
A5 s'posted Edgware, at 2nd roundabout 1m

**4**
**G2** Northway Service Station, Hendon, (H. 3834)
Chevron 07.30-19.30 (10.00-16.00 Sun), petrol, AA bkdn, serv & rprs normal hours
A5 s'posted Edgware, at 1st roundabout ¼m

**6**
**G3** Sheepcote Service Station, Sheepcote
(Garston 74166). Petrol 24hr, 24hr AA/RAC bkdn serv, serv & rprs
A405 s'posted Watford, into village 1½m

**6**
**G4** Chequers Service Station, Birkett Wood
(Garston 72051). Esso. 07.00-22.30, petrol, AA bkdn, serv & rprs normal hours
A405 s'posted St Albans ¼m

**9**
**G5** Watling Street Service Station, Flamstead
Shell. 07.00-21.00 (08.00-20.00 Sun), petrol, derv
A5 s'posted Dunstable ¼m

**11**
**G6** Jet Filling Station, Luton
Jet. 07.00-23.00 (08.00-22.00 Sun), petrol
A505 s'posted Luton ¼m

## PUBS

**6**
**P1**
**(R)** Crown, Garston
Ind Coope; lunch 12.30-14.00, dinner 19.30-22.00, good food, snacks
A405 s'posted Watford 1m

**10**
**P2** Fox, Kinsbourne Green (Harpenden 3817)
Ind Coope; village pub; light lunches, basket meals in evening (exc Wed), trad beer, garden
A6 s'posted Harpenden 2m

**11**
**P3** Norman King, Dunstable (D.61663)
Whitbread; thatched; lunches & dinners in grillroom (exc Sun)
A505 s'posted Dunstable 2½m

**12**
**P4**
**(R)** Star, Chalton (Toddington 2248)
Old beamed pub, non-stop buffet, lunch 12.00-14.00 (exc Sun), dinner 19.00-22.30, garden
A5120 s'posted Dunstable 1¾m

**12**
**P5** Oddfellows Arms, Toddington (T. 52021)
Watneys; businessman's lunch Mon-Fri, snacks, small yard with tables
A5120 s'posted Dunstable, on village green 1m

## RESTAURANTS

**4**
**R1** Dick Turpin, Edgware
Old black-and-white building; lunches & dinners
A5 s'posted Edgware 1½m

## HOTELS

**12**
**H1**
**(R)** Hendon Hall Hotel, Hendon(01-203-3341)
Freehouse; once David Garrick's home, now *** hotel, 56 bedrms with TV, most with bath, lounge, restaurant, bar meals, garden; bkfst 07.30-09.30, lunch 12.30-14.15, dinner 19.00-21.30, t d'hote & a la c, Sunday lunch
Sbound: slip road at Junct 2 to A41, L at lights, ¼m; Nbound: 1m N of North Circular

**6**
**H2**
**(R)** Noke Hotel, St Albans (St A.54252)
Scottish & Newcastle; *** hotel in own grounds, 56 bedrms with TV & bath, restaurant, bar meals; bkfst 07.30-09.30, lunch 12.30-14.00, dinner 19.00-21.45, t d'hote & a la c
A405 s'posted St Albans 1m

**8**
**H3**
**(R)** Post House, Hemel Hempstead (HH.51122)
Trust House Forte; ***91 bedrms with TV & bath, foyer lounge, restaurant, snacks in garden; bkfst 07.00-10.00, lunch 12.30-14.00, dinner 19.00-22.00, t d'hote & a la c, Sunday lunch, buttery 07.00-22.00 for snacks
A414 s'posted Hemel Hempstead ¼m

**11**
**H4**
**(R)** Crest Motel, Luton (Luton 55955)
Bass; *** 138 bedrms with TV & bath, bar snacks; bkfst 07.30-10.00, lunch 12.30-14.00, dinner 18.30-21.45 (19.00-21.30 Sun), t d'hote & a la c, Sunday lunch
A505 s'posted Luton ¼m

# M1. JUNCTIONS 13–16

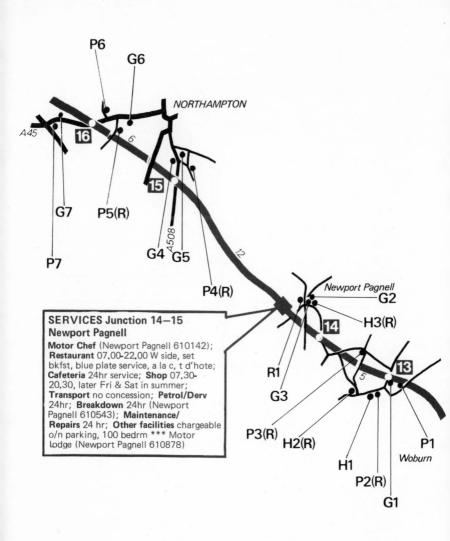

SERVICES Junction 14–15
Newport Pagnell
**Motor Chef** (Newport Pagnell 610142);
**Restaurant** 07.00-22.00 W side, set
bkfst, blue plate service, a la c, t d'hote;
**Cafeteria** 24hr service; **Shop** 07.30-
20.30, later Fri & Sat in summer;
**Transport** no concession; **Petrol/Derv**
24hr; **Breakdown** 24hr (Newport
Pagnell 610543); **Maintenance/
Repairs** 24 hr; **Other facilities** chargeable
o/n parking, 100 bedrm *** Motor
Lodge (Newport Pagnell 610878)

## GARAGES

**13**
**G1** **Halt Garage, Husborne Crawley** (Woburn
Sands 583247). Mobil. 08.00-22.30
(10.00-22.30 Sun), petrol, 24hr AA/
RAC bkdn serv (Milton Keynes 678162
night), serv & rprs 08.00-22.30 (10.00-
22.30 Sun), spares, Avis car hire
B557 s'posted Bletchley          ½m

**14**
**G2** **Tickford Street Filling Station, Newport
Pagnell.** BP. 07.30-22.00 (08.30-22.00
Sun), petrol, derv, shop, limited spares
A5130 s'posted Newport Pagnell, in
town centre          2m

**14**
**G3** **Goose Garage, Newport Pagnell**
Mobil. 07.30-22.30 (09.00-22.00 Sun),
petrol, derv, bkdn & rprs normal hours,
spares, Chrysler agent
A5130 s'posted Newport Pagnell, in
town centre          2m

**15**
**G4** **Collingtree Filling Station, Wootton**
BP. 07.30-22.30 (09.00-22.30 Sun),
petrol, limited spares
A508 s'posted Northampton, on R   ½m

**15** **Wootton Service Station, Wootton**
(Northampton 61658). Esso.07.00-20.00
**G5** (07.30-20.00 Sun), bkdn & rprs normal
hours, shop, spares
A508 s'posted Northampton, to r'bout
1m

**16** **G. White, Kislingbury** (Northampton
830770). Total. 08.00-21.00 (09.30-
**G6** 21.00 Sun), petrol, derv, propane, 24hr
AA/RAC bkdn serv (Northampton
830770 night)
A45 s'posted Northampton, on R    1½m

**16** **Green, Flore** (Weedon 40287)
Shell. 08.00-19.00 (24hr self serv), 24hr
**G7** AA/RAC bkdn serv, serv & rprs normal
hours, Leyland agent, spares
A45 s'posted Daventry, on R    2m

## PUBS

**13** **Rose and Crown, Ridgmont** (Ridgmont
245) Charles Wells; 17C village pub, 1
**P1** rm B&B, bar meals, dinner bookable,
trad ale, garden, camping and caravan site
B557 s'posted Bletchley, L on B559,
in village    1½m

**13** **Bell, Apsley Guise** (Woburn Sands
582263) Ind Coope; village pub, 2 rms
**P2** B&B, lunch 12.00-14.00, dinner
**(R)** 19.00-21.30 exc Mon & Tues, garden
B557 s'posted Bletchley, in village    1½m

**13** **Swan, Salford** (Woburn Sands 583254)
Whitbread; small village pub, lunch
**P3** 12.00-14.15 exc Sun, continental
**(R)** cooking Thurs, Fri, & Sat evening, home-
cooked food, garden
B557 s'posted Bedford, immediate L
s'posted Salford, then L in village    2m

**15** **Queen Eleanor, Wootton**
Watneys; modern roadhouse, lunch
**P4** 12.00-14.00, dinner 19.00-22.00, a la c,
**(R)** grills, cold table, bar snacks, garden
A508 s'posted Northampton, R at
r'bout    1½m

**16** **Cromwell, Kislingbury** (Northampton
830288) Watneys; olde worlde, lunch
**P5** 12.00-14.30, dinner 19.00-22.00 exc
**(R)** Sun, t d'hote, bar snacks, garden
A45 s'posted Northampton, R on B4525
1¼m

**16** **Paddock, Harpole** (Northampton
830588) Courage; modern pub, extensive
**P6** bar, lunch 12.00-14.15, dinner 18.30-
22.00, grills, disco Fri & Sat, folk night
Mon, games room
A45 s'posted Northampton, at junction of
road to village    ½m

**16** **White Hart, Flore** (Weedon 40309)
Watneys; old coaching stage, lunch 12.00-
**P7** 14.00 (cold buffet Sun), dinner 19.00-
22.00 grills (exc Sun & Mon), covered
yard for children
A45 s'posted Daventry, on L    2m

## RESTAURANTS

**14** **Glovers, Newport Pagnell** (Goldcrest 6398)
18C building, cocktail bar, lunch Mon-Fri
**R1** t d'hote & a la c, dinner Tues-Sat a la c
A5130 s'posted Newport Pagnell, in town
centre    2m

## HOTELS

**13** **Holt House, Apsley Guise** (Woburn Sands
583652). Freehouse; small hotel in own
**H1** grounds, 12 rooms B&B, lunches & meals
in cellar bar
B557 s'posted Bletchley, in village    1½m

**13** **Swan, Woburn Sands** (W.S. 583204)
Watneys; old house now *hotel, 12 rooms
**H2** B&B, lunch 12.00-13.30 t d'hote & a la c,
**(R)** dinner 19.00-21.00 a la c, bar snacks
B557 s'posted Bletchley, to A5130, in
town centre    2½m

**14** **Swan Revived, Newport Pagnell** (N.P.
610565)
**H3** Watneys; 17C coaching house modernised,
**(R)** **hotel, 32 bedrms with bath/shower &
TV, residents lounge, lunch 12.00-14.00,
dinner 19.30-21.45, a la c & t d'hote
Sunday lunch
A5130 s'posted Newport Pagnell, R at
junction, on R    2m

# M1. JUNCTIONS 16/17-23

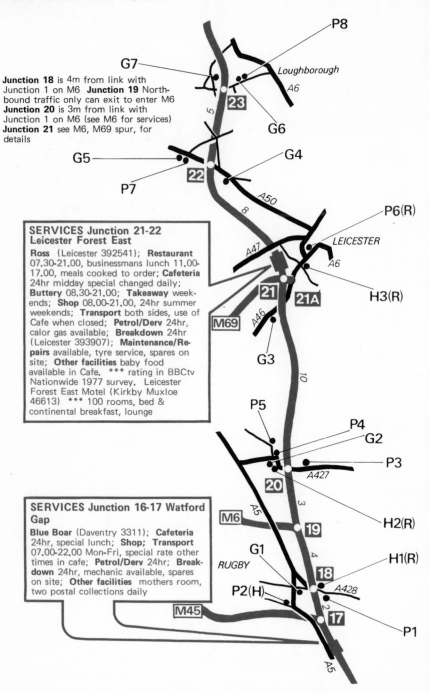

**Junction 18** is 4m from link with Junction 1 on M6  **Junction 19** Northbound traffic only can exit to enter M6  **Junction 20** is 3m from link with Junction 1 on M6 (see M6 for services)  **Junction 21** see M6, M69 spur, for details

P8

G7

*Loughborough*

*A6*

23

G6

G5

22

G4

P7

*A50*

5

8

P6(R)

*LEICESTER*

*A6*

*A47*

21

21A

H3(R)

M69

*A46*

G3

10

SERVICES Junction 21-22
Leicester Forest East

**Ross** (Leicester 392541); **Restaurant** 07.30-21.00, businessmans lunch 11.00-17.00, meals cooked to order; **Cafeteria** 24hr midday special changed daily; **Buttery** 08.30-21.00; **Takeaway** weekends; **Shop** 08.00-21.00, 24hr summer weekends; **Transport** both sides, use of Cafe when closed; **Petrol/Derv** 24hr, calor gas available; **Breakdown** 24hr (Leicester 393907); **Maintenance/Repairs** available, tyre service, spares on site; **Other facilities** baby food available in Cafe. *** rating in BBCtv Nationwide 1977 survey. Leicester Forest East Motel (Kirkby Muxloe 46613) *** 100 rooms, bed & continental breakfast, lounge

P5

P4

G2

P3

20

*A427*

SERVICES Junction 16-17 Watford Gap

**Blue Boar** (Daventry 3311); **Cafeteria** 24hr, special lunch; **Shop; Transport** 07.00-22.00 Mon-Fri, special rate other times in cafe; **Petrol/Derv** 24hr; **Breakdown** 24hr, mechanic available, spares on site; **Other facilities** mothers room, two postal collections daily

H2(R)

3

M6

*A5*

19

H1(R)

G1

*RUGBY*

18

*A428*

P2(H)

*A5*

M45

17

P1

2

4

*A5*

# GARAGES

**18** **Halfway Garage, Kilsby**
Esso. Petrol 24hr self serv, Fiat agent
**G1** A428 s'posted Rugby, at crossroad with
A5 ½m

**20** **Burtons Garage, Lutterworth** (L. 2362)
Shell. Petrol, AA/RAC bkdn, serv &
**G2** rprs normal hours
A427 s'posted Lutterworth, R on A426
1m

**21** **Clarkes Garage, Narborough** (N. 3638)
Shell. 07.00-19.00, limited at wkends,
**G3** petrol, serv & rprs, Renault agent
A46M s'posted Leicester, R on A46
s'posted Coventry 1m

**22** **Field Head Garage, Field Head** (Markfield 2381). Esso. Petrol, serv & rprs
**G4** normal hours.
A50 s'posted Leicester, on R 1m

**22** **Flying Horse Garage, Markfield** (M. 2369)
Mobil. 07.00-21.00 (09.00-21.00 Sun),
**G5** petrol, derv, 24hr bkdn (Markfield 3618
nights), serv & rprs normal hours, spares,
shop
A50 s'posted Ashby, on R ½m

**23** **Temple Filling Station, Thorpe Acre**
Shell. 07.00-21.00 (09.00-20.00 Sun),
**G6** A512 s'posted Loughborough, on L ¼m

**23** **Gavendon Motors, Shepshed** (S. 2287)
Shell. 08.00-18.00 (closed Sun), petrol,
**G7** bkdn serv, rprs normal hours, spares,
Leyland agent.
A512 s'posted Ashby, R to village centre
1m

# PUBS

**18** **Red Lion, Crick** (C. 822343)
Watneys; light lunches & grills
**P1** A428 s'posted Daventry, A428 s'posted
Northampton ¾m

**18** **George, Kilsby** (Rugby 822229)
Bass; quaint roadside pub, 6 rms B&B,
**P2** lunch and evening (19.30-22.15) grills,
**(H)** garden
A428 s'posted Rugby, L on A5, in
village 1½m

**20** **Tavern, Walcote** (Lutterworth 3338)
Freehouse; 19th century coaching house,
**P3** bar meals lunchtime 11.30-14.00 and
evenings 17.30 until ½ hr before closing
time (19.00 Sun), garden, car park
A427 s'posted Market Harborough, on L
in village 1m

**20** **Hind Hotel, Lutterworth** (L. 2341)
Freehouse; old coaching house in town
**P4** centre, B&B, lunch, bar snacks
A427 s'posted Lutterworth ¾m

**20** **Man at Arms, Bitteswell** (Lutterworth
2541) Davenport; 17C, light bar
**P5** lunches, evening snacks, childrens room
in day, trad beer, garden
A427 s'posted Lutterworth, R on B577
2m

**21** **Braunston Inn, Leicester** (L. 824418)
Everards; character pub on main road,
**P6** bar lunches Mon-Sat, restaurant with
**(R)** limited but good grill, 11.00-14.30 &
19.00-23.30
A46 s'posted Leicester, on L in town
2m

**22** **Flying Horse, Markfield** (M. 2842)
Tetley; crossroads pub, lunch 12.00-
**P7** 14.00 Mon-Fri, evening grill 19.30-22.00
A50 s'posted Leicester, on R ½m

**23** **Sea Around Us, Thorpe Acre**
Courage; modern building, lunch 12.00-
**P8** 13.45, snacks other times
A512 s'posted Loughborough, on L 1m

# HOTELS

**18** **Post House, Albion, Crick** (C.822101)
Trust House Forte; modern, 100
**H1** bedrms with TV & bath, lounge, bkfst
**(R)** 07.00-10.00, buttery 13.00-22.00,
lunch 12.00-14.00, dinner 19.00-22.30,
t d'hote & a la c, Sunday lunch, dinner
dance Sat, jazz Fri, package weekend
break, skittles
A428 s'posted Rugby, A428 s'posted
Northampton, on L ¼m

**20** **Denbigh Arms Hotel, Lutterworth**
(L. 3537) Freehouse; modernised
**H2** coaching house, 25 bedrms with TV,
**(R)** most with bath, lounge, trad beer, bkfst
08.00-09.30, lunch 12.30-14.00, dinner
19.00-22.00, t d'hote & a la c, Sunday
lunch, dinner dance Sat
A427 s'posted Lutterworth, on L ¾m

**21** **Post House Motor Motel, Leicester**
(L. 896688). Trust House Forte; modern
**H3** 176 bedrms with TV & bath, foyer
**(R)** lounge, buttery 07.00-22.00 for bkfst
and snacks, restaurant, lunch 12.30-14.30
dinner 19.00-22.00, t d'hote & a la c,
dinner dance alt Sats, music in restaurant
Fri & Sat evenings
A46 s'posted Leicester, on R at 1st
crossing 1¼m

# M1. JUNCTIONS 24-29

**Junction 29** Hardwick Hall, National
Trust property; can be seen on E side of
Motorway between Junctions 28 & 29

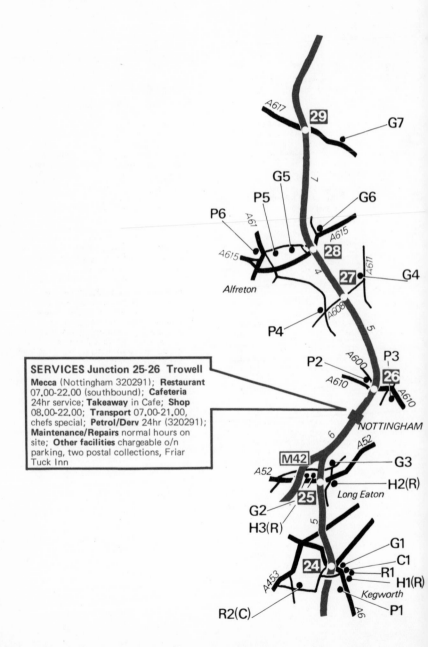

**SERVICES Junction 25-26  Trowell**
**Mecca** (Nottingham 320291); **Restaurant**
07.00-22.00 (southbound); **Cafeteria**
24hr service; **Takeaway** in Cafe; **Shop**
08.00-22.00; **Transport** 07.00-21.00,
chefs special; **Petrol/Derv** 24hr (320291);
**Maintenance/Repairs** normal hours on
site; **Other facilities** chargeable o/n
parking, two postal collections, Friar
Tuck Inn

## CAFES

**24**
**C1** **Trent House Cafe, Kegworth**
08.00-17.00 Mon-Fri, lunches, home cooking, cakes and pastries
A6 s'posted Loughborough, in village on L ½m

## GARAGES

**24**
**G1** **Kegworth Service Station, Kegworth**
(K. 2557). Mobil. 08.00-18.30 (08.00-18.30 Sat, closed Sun), petrol, rprs & bkdn, spares & accessories
A6 s'posted Loughborough, in village ½m

**25**
**G2** **Risley Garage, Risley** (Sandiacre 3174)
Shell, 08.00-18.00. petrol, AA bkdn, serv & rprs normal hours
A52 s'posted Derby, B5010 to village ¾m

**25**
**G3** **Sandiacre Service Station, Sandiacre**
(S. 2497). 08.00-18.00 (09.00-18.00 Sun), 24hr bkdn serv (S.5349 night), serv & rprs normal hours
A52 s'posted Nottingham, 1st L, at junction with B5010 ½m

**27**
**G4** **Underwood Garage, Underwood**
Mobil 07.00-21.00 (08.00-21.00 Sun), petrol, serv & rprs normal hours.
A608 s'posted Hucknall, L onto A611 on L 2½m

**28**
**G5** **Autopart, South Normanton**
(Ripley 811268) Texaco. 08.00-19.00 (10.00-16.00 Sun), petrol, AA bkdn, serv & rprs normal hours, Saab & Honda agency, limited spares
A615 s'posted Matlock, B6019 s'posted Alfreton, on R ¾m

**28**
**G6** **Ashfield Service Station, Sutton Ashfield.** (Mansfield 57355) Texaco. 07.00-20.00 (09.00-16.00 Sun), petrol, RAC bkdn, serv & rprs normal hours
A615 s'posted Mansfield, on L 2m

**29**
**G7** **Red House Service Station, Heath**
(Chesterfield 850329) BP. 08.00-22.00, petrol, AA/RAC bkdn serv, gen rprs 08.00-22.00, spares
A617 s'posted Mansfield, on L 1½m

## PUBS

**24**
**P1** **White House, Kegworth**
Bass; riverside mock Tudor serving lunches, snacks available
A6 s'posted Loughborough, through village 2m

**26**
**P2** **Three Ponds, Nutall** (Nottingham 383170)
Hardy & Hanson; a rebuilt pub, lunch 11.30-14.00 Mon-Fri, wide choice of rolls, snacks evenings & weekends, trad ale, childrens room, garden
A610 s'posted Ilkeston, R at roundabout under bridge ¼m

**26**
**P3** **Red Lion, Cinderhill, Nottingham**
Lunch 12.30-14.00 Mon-Fri, snacks all other times
A610 s'posted Nottingham, R at junction, on L 1½m

**27**
**P4** **Hole in the Wall, Underwood** (Langley Mill 3936) Freehouse; dining room serving lunches and dinners
A608 s'posted Derby, R into village 2½m

**28**
**P5** **King Alfred, Alfreton** (A. 3274)
Home; old fashioned town pub, beamed bars, 5 bedrms for B&B with h & c, snacks in bar
A615 s'posted Matlock, B6019 to village, on L 2½m

**28**
**P6** **George, Alfreton** (A. 2015)
Tetleys; Georgian town pub, 6 rooms B&B, bar lunches Mon-Fri
W on A615 to village at junction 2½m

## RESTAURANTS

**24**
**R1** **Cottage Restaurant, Kegworth**
(K. 2449) Thatched cottage in high street, dinners only 19.00-22.00 (exc Sun & Mon) t d'hote
A6 s'posted Loughborough, L on A5129 ½m

**24**
**R2**
**(C)** **East Midlands Airport, Main Terminal**
(Derby 81062) restaurant overlooking runway, 12.00-21.00 (12.00-18.00 Sun), lunch a la c & t d'hote, bar, high teas, quick-service cafe 06.00-22.00
A6 s'posted East Midlands Airport, R on A5129 2m

## HOTELS

**24**
**H1**
**(R)** **Yew Lodge, Kegworth** (K. 2518)
Freehouse; enlarged private house, 38 bedrms with TV, foyer lounge, restaurant, lunch 12.00-14.00, dinner 18.30-21.30 (19.30-21.30 Sun) a la c, gallery steak bar 12.00-14.00, 18.30-23.00 (exc Sun), dinner dance Fri & Sat
A6 s'posted Loughborough ½m

**25**
**H2**
**(R)** **Post House, Sandiacre**
(Nottingham 397800)
Trust House Forte; *** 107 bedrms with TV & bath, foyer lounge, restaurant, bkfst 07.30-10.00, lunch 12.30-14.30, t d'hote & a la c, dinner a la c (weekends t d'hote also), buttery 07.30-22.00 for quick substantial meals, trad Sun lunch, dinner dance Fri & Sat, breakaway weekends, patio
A52 s'posted Nottingham, on R ¼m

**25**
**H3**
**(R)** **Novotel, Long Eaton** (L.E. 60106)
Freehouse; ***110 bedrms with TV & bath, foyer lounge, restaurant 06.00-24.00 French & English, t d'hote & a la c, open air swimming pool, beer garden, childrens play area
A52 s'posted Derby, R on slip road ¼m

# M1. JUNCTIONS 30-33
## M18 ROTHERHAM — GOOLE   JUNCTIONS 1-2
## A1 (M) DONCASTER BYPASS

**Junction 32 M18 Spur** to link with A1(M)
(Doncaster Bypass) will continue to
**Junction 35 on M62** with 6 junctions.
See M62 for last 2 junctions. **Junction 2,
M18,** for Doncaster Racecourse

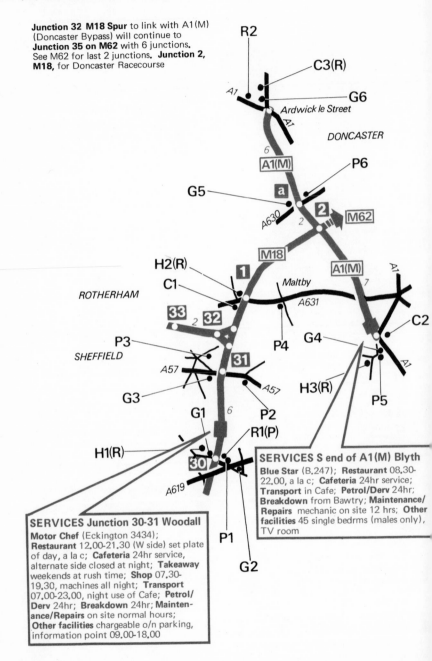

R2

C3(R)

A1

G6

Ardwick le Street

DONCASTER

A1

6

A1(M)

P6

G5

a

A630

2

2

M62

M18

A1(M)

A1

H2(R)

1

Maltby

7

C1

A631

ROTHERHAM

33   2   32

C2

P4

G4

A1

P3

SHEFFIELD

31

H3(R)

A57

P5

G3

A57

P2

G1   6

R1(P)

H1(R)

SERVICES S end of A1(M) Blyth

30

**Blue Star** (B.247); **Restaurant** 08.30-
22.00, a la c; **Cafeteria** 24hr service;
**Transport** in Cafe; **Petrol/Derv** 24hr;
**Breakdown** from Bawtry; **Maintenance/
Repairs** mechanic on site 12 hrs; **Other
facilities** 45 single bedrms (males only),
TV room

A619

SERVICES Junction 30-31 Woodall

**Motor Chef** (Eckington 3434);
**Restaurant** 12.00-21.30 (W side) set plate
of day, a la c; **Cafeteria** 24hr service,
alternate side closed at night; **Takeaway**
weekends at rush time; **Shop** 07.30-
19.30, machines all night; **Transport**
07.00-23.00, night use of Cafe; **Petrol/
Derv** 24hr; **Breakdown** 24hr; **Mainten-
ance/Repairs** on site normal hours;
**Other facilities** chargeable o/n parking,
information point 09.00-18.00

P1

G2

## CAFES

**18/1** **Little Chef, Bramley**
**C1** Trust House Forte; 24hr grills and snacks
A631 s'posted Rotherham, on L ¼m

**1(M)** **Blyth Transport Cafe, Blyth**
**End** 24hr service, meals and snacks, transport
B&B with evening meal, closed 12.00
**C2** Sat-21.00 Sun
On A614 Bawtry road ½m

**1(M)** **Haven Cafe/ Restaurant, Skellow**
**End** (Doncaster 723520). 24hr transport
**C3** cafe, full meals 11.00-19.30, substantial
**(R)** snacks other times, transport B&B with
evening meal, restaurant 10.00-18.00,
a la c, shop
On A1 dual carriageway ½m

## GARAGES

**30** **Bridge House Garage, Reneshaw**
**G1** (Chesterfield 810677). Total. 07.00-
21.00 (09.00-21.00 Sun), AA/RAC
bkdn, serv & rprs
A616 s'posted Sheffield, on L 1m

**30** **Elf Garage, Clowne**
**G2** Elf. 09.00-21.00 (10.30-18.00 Sun),
petrol, serv & rprs
A616 s'posted Newark, on R 1m

**31** **Aston Filling Station, Aston**
**G3** Amoco. 07.00-22.00 (09.00-21.00 Sun),
self serv petrol
A57 s'posted Sheffield, L at 1st junction
1m

**1(M)** **Holmgate Motor Company, Blyth**
**End** (B. 273) 08.00-18.00 (10.30-13.00 Sun),
petrol, 24hr bkdn, serv & rprs, spares
**G4** On B6045 in village ½m

**1(M)** **Warmsworth Service Station**
**a** (Doncaster 853249)Texaco. 07.00-23.00,
petrol, bkdn 07.00-23.00, serv & rprs
**G5** normal hours, Leyland agent
A630 s'posted Rotherham, on R ½m

**1(M)** **Supreme White, Skellow**
**End** 24hr self serv, spares
**G6** On A1 dual carriageway ¼m

## PUBS

**30** **Rose and Crown, Barlborough**
**P1** (Chesterfield 810364). Bass (Stones);
old pub modernised, lunches Mon-Fri,
dinners Tue-Fri, basket meals at
weekends, sandwiches, trad ale
A619 s'posted Worksop, L into village
¼m

**31** **Red Lion, Todwick**
**P2** Roadside pub with grill, lunch 12.00-
14.00 (exc Sat), dinner 19.00-22.00,
garden
A57 s'posted Worksop ¾m

**31** **Royal Oak, Ulley**
**P3** Picturesque old farmhouse, lunch 12.00-
14.00 Mon-Fri, evening grills, garden
A57 s'posted Sheffield, R into Spinkhill,
R fork in village 1m

**18/1** **Lumley Arms, Maltby**
**P4** Sam Smith; Victorian, steak bar, bar
lunches and snacks, tables outside
A631 s'posted Maltby 2½m

**A1(M)** **Angel, Blyth** (B. 213)
**S End** Kimberley; small village hotel, 8 rooms
B&B, varied bar meals, lunch 12.00-14.00,
**P5** dinner 19.00-21.00, childrens room,
garden
On B6045 in village ½m

**A1(M)** **Winning Post, Balby** (Doncaster 853493)
**a** John Smith; modern pub, lunch 12.00-
14.00 Mon-Fri, evening meals
**P6** A630 s'posted Doncaster, on L ¼m

## RESTAURANTS

**30** **Royal Oak, Barlborough** (Chesterfield
**R1** 810425). Bass (Stones); 17C, lunch
**(P)** 12.00-14.00, dinner 19.00-22.00 (19.00-
22.30 weekends), t d'hote, a la c, bar
meals, trad ale
A619 s'posted Worksop, L into village
¼m

**A1(M)** **Hampole Priory, Hampole** (Doncaster
**N End** 713740) 17C site of old priory, small
**R2** family restaurant, a la c dinners only,
19.00-21.30 Tue-Sat, garden
A638 s'posted Wakefield, R into hamlet
1m

## HOTELS

**30** **Park Hall, Spinkhill** (Eckington 3285)
**H1** Freehouse; 17C manor house, 8 bedrms
**(R)** with bath & TV, restaurant, lunch (exc
Sat) t d'hote, dinners (exc Sat) a la c,
dinner dances most Sat, extensive
garden, trad beer
A616 s'posted Sheffield, R into village,
L down track 1½m

**M 18/1** **Elton Hotel, Bramley** (Wickersley 5681)
**H2** Converted private house in own grounds,
**(R)** 16 bedrms, lounge, bar restaurant, lunches
and dinners, t d'hote & a la c
A631 s'posted Rotherham, on R ½m

**A1(M)** **Fourways, Blyth**
**S End** Freehouse; ** Georgian building,
**H3** 9 bedrms, restaurant, lunch 12.00-14.00,
**(R)** dinner 19.00-21.00
On crossroads of B6045 & A634 in village
¾m

# **M1.** JUNCTIONS 34-END

**Junction 34** has 2 parts linked by a dual carriageway under the main Motorway

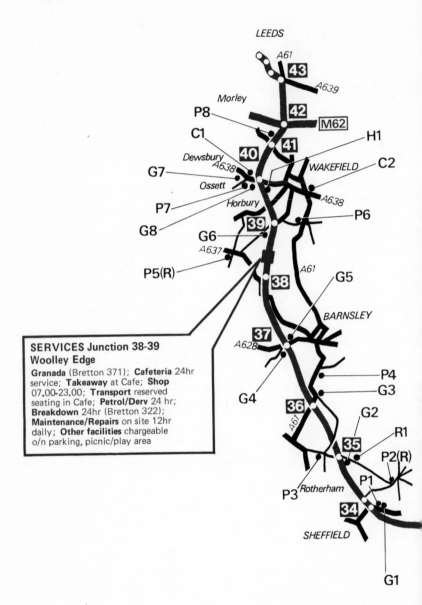

LEEDS

*A61*

**43**

*A639*

Morley

**P8**

**42**

M62

**C1**

**41**

**H1**

Dewsbury

**40**

WAKEFIELD

**C2**

*A638*

**G7**

Ossett

*A638*

**P7**

Horbury

**P6**

**G8**

**39**

**G6**

*A637*

**P5(R)**

**38**

*A61*

**G5**

BARNSLEY

**SERVICES Junction 38-39**
**Woolley Edge**
**Granada** (Bretton 371); **Cafeteria** 24hr
service; **Takeaway** at Cafe; **Shop**
07.00-23.00; **Transport** reserved
seating in Cafe; **Petrol/Derv** 24 hr;
**Breakdown** 24hr (Bretton 322);
**Maintenance/Repairs** on site 12hr
daily; **Other facilities** chargeable
o/n parking, picnic/play area

**37**

*A628*

**P4**

**G3**

**G4**

**36**

**G2**

*A61*

**35**

**R1**

**P2(R)**

**P3** Rotherham

**P1**

**34**

**G1**

SHEFFIELD

## CAFES

**40**
**C1**
**Bridge Cafe, Flushdyke**
08.00-16.30 (08.00-23.00 Sat, closed Sun), substantial snacks
A638 s'posted Dewsbury, L on B6128, loop road to village                    ½m

**40**
**C2**
**White Rose, Wakefield** (W. 77939)
08.00-19.00 Mon-Fri, light meals and snacks (open weekends in summer)
A638 s'posted Wakefield                    2m

## GARAGES

**34**
**G1**
**Murco Filling Station, Tinsley**
Murco. 07.00-22.00, petrol self serv
A6178 s'posted Doncaster, A631 s'posted Maltby, on L                    ½m

**35**
**G2**
**Scholes Service Station, Thorpe Hesley**
(Ecclesfield 4088). Fina. 08.00-19.00 petrol, derv, bkdn, serv & rprs normal hours
A629 s'posted Rotherham, on L      ½m

**36**
**G3**
**Sovereign, Birdwell** (Barnsley 742064)
Rico. 08.00-18.00 (exc Sun), petrol, 24hr bkdn (Barnsley 754643 night), mechanical rprs and bodywork
A61 s'posted Barnsley, on R      ¼m

**37**
**G4**
**Motorway Filling Station**
Shell. 08.00-22.00 (09.00-14.00 Sun) petrol, derv
A628 s'posted Manchester, on L      ¼m

**37**
**G5**
**Danway Motors, Dodworth**
(Barnsley 87347)
Shell. 08.00-22.00 (09.00-19.00 Sun) petrol, derv, bkdn, rprs normal hours
A628 s'posted Barnsley, on L      ¼m

**39**
**G6**
**Grove Filling Station, Calders Grove**
(Horbury 274756). Elf. 07.00-19.00 (09.00-16.00 Sun), serv, rprs & bkdn normal hours
A636 s'posted Huddersfield, on R      ¼m

**40**
**G7**
**Bridge Garage, Flushdyke** (Ossett 273368) Globe. 08.00-19.00, closed Sunday, petrol, derv, 24hr bkdn, rprs
A638 s'posted Dewsbury, L on B6128, loop road to village                    ½m

**40**
**G8**
**Highway Recovery, Ossett**
(Wakefield 77219) Texaco; 09.00-18.00 daily, towing recovery, RAC get you home service
A638 s'posted Dewsbury, L on B6128, loop road to village                    ½m

## PUBS

**34**
**P1**
**Pike and Heron, Tinsley** (Sheffield 42916)
Mansfield; suburbs pub, lunches Mon-Fri & Sun, evening meals 19.30-22.30, mainly grills
A6178 s'posted Doncaster, A631 s'posted Maltby, on L                    ¾m

**34**
**P2**
**(R)**
**Drawbridge, Kimberworth**
(Rotherham 79626) Stones; purpose built, cold buffet lunches in bar, restaurant, lunch 12.00-14.00 Mon-Fri, dinner 19.30-22.30 (exc Mon)
A6109 s'posted Rotherham, L on A629                    1½m

**35**
**P3**
**Crown & Cushion, Chapeltown**
(Ecclesfield 4600). John Smith; small 18C pub, lunches Mon-Fri 12.00-14.00, grills in the evenings, seats outside
A629 s'posted Penistone, past crossroads, on L                    1½m

**36**
**P4**
**Red Lion, Worsbrough** (Barnsley 82639)
John Smith; old coaching house, 7 rooms B&B with evening meal, lunches (exc Sat), Sunday lunch, snacks other times, beer garden, childrens play area
A61 s'posted Barnsley, on R                    2m

**39**
**P5**
**(R)**
**Black Bull, Midgeley** (Bretton 260)
Whitbread; pub serving lunches, dinners, restaurant
A636 s'posted Huddersfield, R on A637, in village                    2½m

**39**
**P6**
**Star, Sandal** (Wakefield 55254)
John Smith; quaint old house, lunch 12.00-14.00 Mon-Fri, bar snacks
A636 s'posted Wakefield, R on B6378, in village                    1¼m

**40**
**P7**
**Red Lion, Ossett** (O.3449)
Watneys; small town pub, buffet lunches 12.00-14.00 Mon-Fri, snacks other times
A638 s'posted Dewsbury, L on B6128, at crossroads                    1½m

**41**
**P8**
**New White Bear, Tingley** (Morley 532768)
Watneys Schooner Inns; popular steak house
A650 s'posted Morley, on roundabout   ¼m

## RESTAURANTS

**35**
**R1**
**Grange Park, Dropping Well** (Rotherham 64884). Municipal golf club with public restaurant, lunch Mon-Fri 12.00-14.00, t d'hote & a la c, dinner 19.30-22.30 (exc Mon) a la c, dancing Fri & Sat evenings, disco Tue & Thurs evening
A629 s'posted Rotherham, R down golf course road                    2m

## HOTELS

**40**
**H1**
**Albany, Ossett** (Wakefield 276388)
Trust House Forte; **** purpose built, 96 bedrms with TV & bath, restaurant, t d'hote & a la c, buttery 07.00-23.00 daily, bar, garden, get away weekend terms
A638 s'posted Wakefield, on R overlooking motorway                    ¼m

# M2. Medway Towns
## ROCHESTER (STROUD) — FAVERSHAM

2-lane Motorway; A2 at either end is near Motorway standard (A2 before start is Watling St, the Roman road), M2 bypasses Sittingbourne — the turn-off for the new Sheerness/Holland Ferry; Canterbury 7m from Junction 7 on A2. Picnic area both sides 1m before start of Motorway

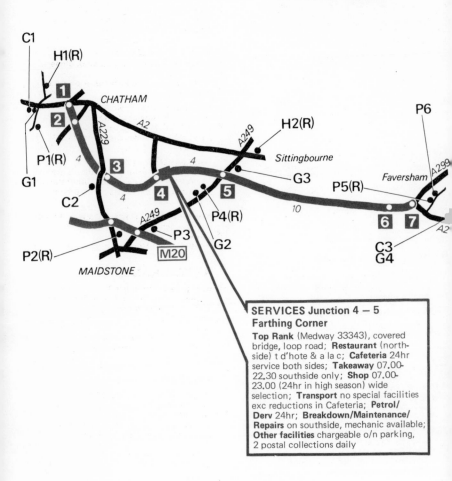

SERVICES Junction 4 — 5
**Farthing Corner**

**Top Rank** (Medway 33343), covered bridge, loop road; **Restaurant** (north-side) t d'hote & a la c; **Cafeteria** 24hr service both sides; **Takeaway** 07.00-22.30 southside only; **Shop** 07.00-23.00 (24hr in high season) wide selection; **Transport** no special facilities exc reductions in Cafeteria; **Petrol/Derv** 24hr; **Breakdown/Maintenance/Repairs** on southside, mechanic available; **Other facilities** chargeable o/n parking, 2 postal collections daily

## CAFES

**End** **Little Chef, Cobham**
**C1** 24hr service, grills and quick meals
A2 before start of M 2m

**3** **Coronation Transport Cafe, Bridgwood**
**C2** 06.30-17.00 (closed 12.00 Sat-Mon am),
bkfst, lunch snacks
A229 s'posted Maidstone ¼m

**End** **Gate Inn Cafe, Dunkirk**
**C3** 24hr transport (06.00-23.00 public)
daily, snacks, light meals
A2 at E end of M 2m

## GARAGES

**End** **Cobham Filling Station, Cobham**
**G1** Esso. 24hr, petrol, derv, windscreen
rprs, both sides, but north side closed
Sat & Sun
A2 before start of M 2m

**5** **Highland Garage, Detling** (Maidstone
**G2** 39864). 07.00-20.00 (08.00-20.00 Sun),
petrol, derv, 24hr AA bkdn serv, serv &
rprs normal hours, spares
A249 s'posted Maidstone, on R 2½m

**5** **Danaway Filling Station, Danaway**
**G3** BP. Petrol 24hr
A249 s'posted Sittingbourne, on R ¼m

**End** **Gate Inn Garage, Dunkirk**
**G4** 07.00-24.00, petrol, derv
A2 at E end of M 2m

## PUBS

**End** **Old Leather Bottle, Cobham** (Gravesend
**P1** 814327). Trumans; Pickwick's famous
**(R)** pub; 4 rms B&B, bar snacks, restaurant,
Sunday lunch, trad beer, garden
B2009 s'posted Cobham off A2 before
start of M 2½m

**3** **Running Horses, Sandling**
**P2** Courage; mock Tudor; lunch 12.00-14.00
**(R)** (exc Sun) t d'hote & a la c, dinner 19.00-
22.00 (exc Sun & Mon) a la c; substantial
quick bar meals, garden
A229 s'posted Maidstone, on L beyond
M20 3m

**5** **Cock Horse Inn, Detling**
**P3** Shepherd & Neame; 17C beamed pub;
light lunches Mon-Fri, snacks weekends
and evenings, trad beer
A249 s'posted Maidstone, L to village
3m

**5** **Three Squirrels, Stockbury Valley**
**P4** (Newington 842449). Courage; 17C
**(R)** lunches & dinners, t d'hote & a la c
(exc Sun & Mon evenings), good bar
snacks, Sunday lunch
A249 s'posted Maidstone, on R 1m

**End** **White Horse, Boughton St** (B. 343)
**P5** Shepherd & Neame; 16C village pub;
**(R)** 4 service flats for B&B; lunch 12.00-
14.00 (exc Sat & Sun), dinner 19.00-
21.30 (exc Tues), cold buffet when
restaurant closed, trad ale, tables on
patio
A2 at E end of M, L into village 1¼m

**5** **Queens Head, Boughton St** (B. 369)
**P6** Shepherd & Neame; Georgian coaching
house; 4 rooms B&B; lunch 12.00-14.00,
dinner 19.00-22.30 (exc Sun), home
cooking, trad beer, children's room,
garden
A2 at E end of M, L into village 1½m

## HOTELS

**W End** **Inn on the Lake, Shorne** (S. 3333)
**H1** Lakeside motel on A2, 78 bedrms with
**(R)** bath & TV, foyer lounge, restaurant,
pop music Mon evenings, country & western
music Tues evenings, garden; bkfst 07.00-
10.00, lunch 12.00-14.00, dinner 19.00-
22.00, t d'hote & a la c, Sunday lunch
A2 before start of M 1m

**5** **Coniston Hotel, Sittingbourne** (S.72907)
**H2** Purpose-built ** 40 bedrms, half with
**(R)** bath, restaurant
A249 s'posted Sittingbourne, R at A2
3m

# M3. London-Southampton

Completion to Winchester delayed (now ends SW of Basingstoke). M3 approached by A316, dual carriageway with roundabouts from Richmond, 4m before M3, very congested at rush hours. Extension planned to Kings Worthy (Winchester) parallel to A33, joining Winchester bypass to M27 (Southampton bypass and planned South Coast Motorway, Dover — Honiton).

**Junction 1** A375 E to **Kempton Park Racecourse & Hampton Court,** W to **London Airport. Junction 2** M25 spur to **London Airport.** Interchange with M3 — SW exit only. M25 South Orbital Motorway will link M23 London-Brighton N of Redhill (junction completed) with M20 Swanley-Folkestone (Dartford Tunnel spur completed). **Junction 3** A322 N to **Windsor**

## PUBS

**6** **Hatch, Hatch** (Basingstoke 3077)
**P1** Courage; modernised old coaching house; lunches 12.00-14.00 Mon-Fri, basket meals other times, live entertainment Wed/Sun evenings, Aunt Sally game, garden
A33 s'posted Newbury, R at r'bout on A30                                1½m

**5** **Swan, North Warnborough** (Odiham 2727)
**P2** Courage; 17C pub used by bargees;
**(R)** lunches (exc Sun & Mon) and dinners, garden
A32 s'posted Farnham, on R next to canal bridge                        2m

**5** **White Hart, Hook** (H. 2462)
**P3** Ind Coope; old coaching house; bar meals, restaurant
A32 s'posted Farnham, to village, fork R, on R                         2m

**4** **White Hart, Frimley** (Camberley 63092)
**P4** Watneys; tile hung; bar lunches Mon-Sat, light evening meals in bar, snacks Sun
A325 s'posted Farnborough            ¼m

**M25** **Bells of Ouzeley, Old Windsor**
**P5** (Windsor 61526) Freehouse; mock
**(R)** Tudor on Thames, restaurant, buffet bar, bar meals, garden
Doubleback from r'bout to feeder road, A308 to Windsor              2¼m

## CAFES

**W End** **Little Chef, Popham** (Dummer 436)
**C1** 24hr service Thurs, Fri, Sat, Sun, July-Sept, 07.00-22.00 otherwise, small shop
A33 at W end of M                      1m

**7** **Blue Hut, Basingstoke** (B. 21352)
**C2** 08.00-17.30 (07.00-24.00 Sat, closed Sun), bkfst, snacks, fried meals, o/n parking
A30 s'posted Basingstoke              ¾m

**3** **Bert's Gone Mad, Bagshot** (B.73193)
**C3** 07.00-22.30 (07.00-14.00 Sat, closed Sun), bkfst, light meals, transport B&B
A322 s'posted Bracknell, L on A30 into Bagshot                         ½m

## RESTAURANTS

**5** **Raven Hotel, Hook** (H. 2541)
**R1** 2 restaurants, lunch 12.00-14.00, dinner
**(H)** 19.00-22.30 (23.00 Fri & Sat), a la c, English & Greek cooking, dinner dances nightly exc Sun, bar meals, accommodation
A32 s'posted Farnham, to village     ½m

**5** **Mill House, North Warnborough**
**R2** (Odiham 2953) Old converted mill; main meals, garden
A32 s'posted Farnham, on R            ¾m

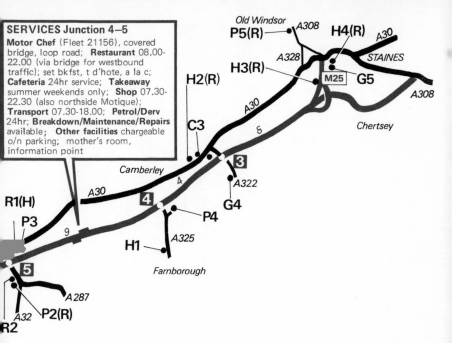

**SERVICES Junction 4–5**
**Motor Chef** (Fleet 21156), covered bridge, loop road; **Restaurant** 08.00-22.00 (via bridge for westbound traffic); set bkfst, t d'hote, a la c; **Cafeteria** 24hr service; **Takeaway** summer weekends only; **Shop** 07.30-22.30 (also northside Motique); **Transport** 07.30-18.00; **Petrol/Derv** 24hr; **Breakdown/Maintenance/Repairs** available; **Other facilities** chargeable o/n parking; mother's room, information point

# GARAGES

**End G1** **Cloverleaf Filling Station, Micheldever** 07.00-21.00 (07.00-23.00 Fri & Sat, 09.00-21.00 Sun), petrol, derv, spares
A30 at W end of M　　　　　　　1m

**End G2** **Popham Service Station, Popham** (Dummer 380) Texaco. 08.00-21.00, petrol, 24hr bkdn serv (Basingstoke 67707 nights), serv & rprs, spares
A33 at W end of M　　　　　　1m

**6 G3** **Cloverleaf Garage, Basing** (Basingstoke 3896) Esso. 06.30-20.30 (8.00-20.00 Sun), AA bkdn, serv normal hours, spares, Fiat & Lancia agent
A33 s'posted Basingstoke, R on A30, on L　　　　　　½m

**3 G4** **Brandon Service Station, Lightwater** (Bagshot 73060) Elf. 07.30-22.00 (09.00-22.00 Sun), petrol, derv, 24hr AA/RAC light bkdn serv, serv & rprs normal hours, Renault agent, spares
A322 s'posted Guildford, R into village　　　　　½m

**25 G5** **Runnymede Service Station, Egham** (E. 4743) 7.30-22.30 (8.00-22.30 Sun), petrol 24hr, AA bkdn serv (Ashford 44742 nights), serv & rprs normal hours, Datsun agent, limited spares
Doubleback from r'bout to feeder road, into Egham village　　　　¼m

# HOTELS

**4 H1** **Tumbledown Dick, Farnborough** (F. 42055) Courage; old coaching house; 10 rooms B&B, bar meals, restaurant
A325 s'posted Farnborough, on R　1m

**3 H2 (R)** **Cricketers, Bagshot** (B. 73196) Trust House Forte; old enlarged coaching house; **26 bedrms with TV, some with bath, lounge, restaurant, bar meals, bargain break weekends, garden; bkfst 07.30-09.30, lunch 12.00-14.00, dinner 19.00-22.00 t d'hote & a la c, Sunday lunch, dinner dance Sats
A322 s'posted Bracknell, L on A30　½m

**M25 H3 (R)** **Great Fosters, Egham** (E. 3822) Elizabethan mansion, now ****hotel, 23 bedrms with bath, TV, some 4-poster beds, lounge, 2 restaurants, dinner dance Sats, swimming, tennis, bkfst 07.30-10.00, lunch 12.00-14.30, dinner 19.30-21.30 t d'hote & a la c, gourmet cooking
Doubleback thro village S of 1-way system　　　　　　　2m

**M25 H4 (R)** **Runnymede Hotel, Egham** (E. 6171) ****90 bedrms with bath, TV, foyer lounge, restaurant, buffet, Thameside bar serving light meals, Sunday lunch, nightly dinner dance, exc Sun, garden, pitch & putt; bkfst 07.15-10.00, lunch 12.30-15.15, dinner 18.30-22.15 t d'hote & a la c
Doubleback from r'bout to feeder road, A308 to Windsor　　　　　¼m

# M4. London - South Wales

## JUNCTIONS 1–11

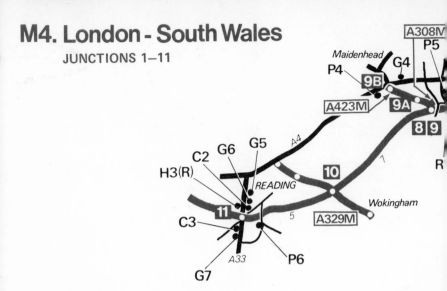

Dual carriageway approach to M4 from Earl's Court with controlled traffic lights allows for quick exit from Central London to London Airport (Heathrow) and the west. Severn Bridge, toll bridge, world's longest suspension bridge, 2-lane (often 1-lane in high winds) very congested at rush hours and holiday weekends. Lorry weight limit 32 tons

**Junction 4** London Airport complex has restaurants, petrol, chargeable parking, numerous hotels of all classes in vicinity. **Junction 5-6** fine views of Windsor Castle to south. **Junction 10 329(M)** spur for Reading East. **Junction 11** link for Southampton via A33 to join M3 at Junction 6

## CAFES

**2**
**C1** Jox's Cafe, Chiswick
07.30-17.00 (08.00-24.00 Sat, closed Sun) home cooking, lunchtime specials, light meals, chargeable o/n parking
Under flyover at start A406 N. Circular                                    ¼m

**11**
**C2** Little Chef, Reading
07.30-23.00, grills, light meals, snacks
A33 s'posted Reading, on R        ¼m

**11**
**C3** Black and White Cafe, Three Mile Cross
08.00-15.30 (closed Sat & Sun), meals and snacks, chargeable o/n parking
A33 s'posted Basingstoke, on R    ¼m

## GARAGES

**2**
**G1** Chiswick Flyover Service Station
(01-994-1119). Esso. Petrol, 24hr self serv, AA ** rprs, service normal hours
Under flyover on L at roundabout   ¼r

**3**
**G2** North Hyde Service Station, Hayes
(01-573-6912). Esso. 07.00-23.00 (08.00-22.00 Sun), AA/RAC bkdn serv (01-882-6481 night), serv & rprs normal hours, limited spares
A312 s'posted Hayes, L at junction, on R                                  ½r

**7**
**G3** Maidenhead Autos, Taplow
(Maidenhead 25131) Shell. Petrol 24hr AA/RAC 24hr bkdn serv
A4 s'posted Slough West, on L      2r

**8 9**
**G4** Boyne Hill Garage, Maidenhead (M.2133: Esso. 08.00-22.30, petrol 24hr prepay, bkdn serv normal hours, Renault & Toyota agent
A423(M) s'posted Maidenhead, R at roundabout onto A4              ¼r

**11**
**G5** Whitley Wood Service Station, Reading
(R.81278) Esso. Petrol 24hr self serv derv, bkdn serv, rprs normal hours, Toyota agent
A33 s'posted Reading, on R          ½r

**11**
**G6** City Filling Station, Reading
Shell. 24hr self serv, limited spares
A33 s'posted Reading, on R          ¼r

**11**
**G7** Hearne Bros, Three Mile Cross
(Reading 883581) 07.30-22.00 (09.00-22.00 Sun) petrol, derv, serv & rprs normal hours, AA bkdn
A33 s'posted Basingstoke, on R     ¼r

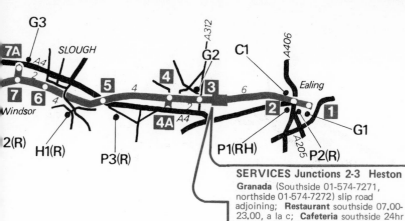

## SERVICES Junctions 2-3 Heston

**Granada** (Southside 01-574-7271, northside 01-574-7272) slip road adjoining; **Restaurant** southside 07.00-23.00, a la c; **Cafeteria** southside 24hr service, dish of the day; **Shop** 07.00-23.00 (summer weekends 24hr); **Transport** 24hr Mon-Fri, northside, special rates in Cafe; **Petrol/Derv** 24hr self service, attendant available; **Breakdown** on call; **Maintenance/Repairs** available normal hours, limited; **Other facilities** chargeable o/n parking, picnic/play area northside, 2 postal collections

## PUBS

**2 P1 (R) (H)** **Coach and Horses, Kew Green**
(01-940-1208) Youngs; colour washed coaching house, known in 1580, 7 bedrms B&B, each with shower, restaurant, bar meals, trad ale, garden
A205 South Circular, at far end of Kew Green ½m

**2 P2 (R)** **City Barge, Strand on the Green**
(01-994-2148) Courage; riverside pub, restaurant, lunch 12.30-14.00 Mon-Fri, bar snacks, seats on the riverbank towpath
A205 South Circular, L before Kew Bridge 1m

**5 P3 (R)** **Ostrich, Colnbrook** (C. 2628)
Freehouse; 17C famous character pub, old beamed bars, informal lunches 10.30-14.30, dinners 18.00-22.30, a la c gourmet standard home cooking
A4 s'posted Colnbrook, in village centre 1¼m

**9 P4** **Shire Horse, Littlewick Green** (LG.53351)
Courage; stabling for Courages famous dray horses, character pub serving lunches (exc Mon), afternoon teas, dinners (exc Mon), Sunday lunch, garden
A423M s'posted Maidenhead, L onto A4 ¼m

**9 P5 (R)** **Hinds Head, Bray** (Maindenhead 26151)
Courage; picturesque old village pub, 7 bedrms, most with bath, restaurant, lunch 12.30-14.30 (12.30-14.00 Sun), dinner 19.30-21.00, t d'hote & a la c, bar meals
A308M, R onto A308, L into village 2m

**11 P6** **Blackboy, Shinfield**
Courage; character pub, light meals Mon-Fri, snacks, trad ale, garden
A33 s'posted Basingstoke, L at lights s'posted Shinfield, L onto A327 2½m

## RESTAURANTS

**8 9 R1** **Waterside Inn, Bray** (Maidenhead 20691) Licenced; old ferrymans house alongside the Thames, closed Mon, lunch 12.30-14.00, dinner 19.30-22.00, t d'hote & a la c, gourmet cooking, mainly French
A308M, R onto A308, L into Bray village, R to river 2m

## HOTELS

**5 H1 (R)** **Manor Hotel, Datchet** (Slough 42893)
Freehouse; ** 20 bedrms with TV, some with bath, restaurant, lunch 12.30-13.45, businessmans lunch, t d'hote & a la c, dinner 19.30-22.00 (19.30-21.30 Sun, Mon), Sunday lunch, French cuisine, grill, bar meals
A4 s'posted Colnbrook, R on B470 to Datchet 2½m

**8 9 H2 (R)** **Monkey Island Hotel, Bray** (Maidenhead 23400) Freehouse; in mid-Thames with own moorings, 25 bedrms with bath & TV, lounge, restaurant, bkfst 07.30-09.00, lunch 12.30-13.45, dinner 19.30-21.45, t d'hote, Sunday lunch, dinner dance Fri & Sat, bar meals, trad beer, garden
A308M, R onto A308, L into Bray, R down lane out of village 2½m

**11 H3 (R)** **Post House, Reading** (R. 85485)
Trust House Forte; 121 bedrms with bath & TV, lounge, restaurant, lunch 12.30-14.30, dinner 19.00-22.30, t d'hote & a la c, buttery, 07.30-22.30, light meals all day, bar, swimming pool, jazz nights Tues, Wed & Sun, garden
A35 s'posted Reading, on L ¼m

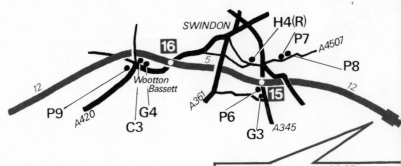

SWINDON H4(R) P7 A4507 P8
16 5
12 Wootton Bassett A361
P9 A420 G4 P6 15
C3 G3 A345
12

Junction 13 Newbury racecourse.
Junction 14 Hungerford, quaint old market town with fascinating Flea Market for antiques

## CAFES

**12 C1 (R)** Regency Coffee Bar and Restaurant, Theale (Reading 302476) 08.00-17.00, bkfst, lunch, light meals, B&B, evening meal
A4 s'posted Theale, on loop road into town, L at junction, on R ½m

**14 C2** Transport Cafe, Eddington, Hungerford 08.00-18.00 (later in summer) closed Sun, snacks & light meals
A338 s'posted Hungerford, R on A4, on R 3m

**16 C3** Coped Hall Transport Cafe, Wootton Bassett 08.00-17.00 (08.00-23.00 Sat, closed Sun), hot meals and snacks
A420 s'posted Wootton Bassett, on R 1½m

## GARAGES

**12 G1** Calcot Filling Station, Calcot 07.30-19.00 (09.00-18.00 Sun), petrol
A4 s'posted Reading, on L ¼m

**14 G2** Normans, Eddington (Hungerford 2033) Total. 06.00-23.00 (08.00-23.00 Sun), petrol, bkdn recovery serv, rprs, spares, Fiat agency
A338 s'posted Hungerford, R on A4, on R 2¾m

**15 G3** Coate Service Garage, Coate (Swindon 27733) Total. 08.00-22.00 (09.00-21.00 Sun), petrol, derv, RAC bkdn, serv & rprs normal hours, spares, shop, vehicle hire
A345 s'posted Marlborough, on R ¼m

**16 G4** Coped Hall Service Station, Wootton Bassett (WB.2755) Esso. 08.00-22.00 (09.00-19.00 Sun), petrol, derv, AA bkdn (WB. 3757 night) serv & rprs normal hours
A420 s'posted Wootton Bassett, on R ¾m

## SERVICES Junctions 14-15 Membury

**Ross** (Lambourn 71881) open connecting bridge & loop road; **Restaurant** buttery 08.00-22.00, basic menu and daily choice; **Cafeteria** 24hr service; **Takeaway** summer weekends; **Shop** 08.00-22.00, 24hr high season; **Transport** 08.00-15.00 Mon-Thurs, special rates in Cafe other times; **Petrol/ Derv** 24hr self service, attendant available; **Breakdown/Maintenance/Repairs** on site during day (Lambourn 71860); **Other facilities** chargeable o/n parking, 3 postal collections weekdays

## PUBS

**12 P1** Travellers Friend, Calcot Ind Coope; village pub, home cooked bar lunches Mon-Fri, snacks other times, trad ale
A4 s'posted Reading, on L ½m

**13 P2 (R)** Red Lion, Chieveley Freehouse; quaint old village pub, small restaurant, mainly grills up to 22.00 (exc Sun & Mon), substantial bar snacks, garden
A34 s'posted Oxford, L into village 1m

**13 P3** Donnington Castle, Donnington (Newbury 40615) Whitbread; old road-side pub, 2 rooms B&B, substantial bar meals (exc Wed evening), trad beer, garden
A34 s'posted Newbury, loop road to village 2½

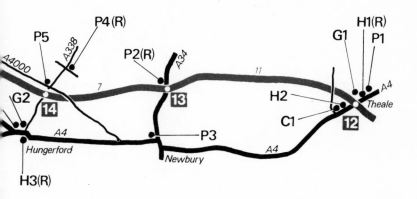

**14** **Swan, Great Shefford** (GS. 287)
**P4** Courage; old coaching house,
**(R)** restaurant overlooking stream, evening
meals 19.00-21.00 (exc Sun), substantial
snacks, Sunday lunch, trad beer, garden
A388 s'posted Wantage, to village, on R
2m

**14** **Pheasant, Shefford Woodlands**
**P5** Freehouse, isolated country pub, bar
meals, evening meals in lounge
A388 s'posted Wantage, L at crossroads
¼m

**15** **Plough, Badbury**
**P6** Arkles; roadside pub, light lunches daily
(exc Sun), evening snacks
A345 s'posted Marlborough, on R    ¼m

**15** **Brewers Arms, Lower Warnborough** (W.338)
**P7** Arkles; attractive village pub, B&B, light
lunches 12.00-14.00 daily, evening meals,
garden, aviary
A419 s'posted Cirencester, R then L
fork, to village, on L    2½m

**15** **Harrow, Lower Warnborough** (W.622)
**8** Whitbread; thatched character pub,
lunches & dinners daily, trad beer, snacks,
garden
A419 s'posted Cirencester, R then L fork,
to village on L at far end    2¾m

**6** **Angel, Wootton Bassett** (WB 2314)
**9** Whitbread; small town pub, B&B, bar
snacks
A420 s'posted Wootton Bassett, L into
town, on R    2m

## HOTELS

**12** **Calcot Hotel, Calcot** (Reading 27297)
**H1** Freehouse; country hotel in own
**(R)** grounds, 20 bedrms, some with showers
& TV, restaurant, lunch 12.00-14.00,
dinner 19.00-21.00, t d'hote, & a la c,
summer buffet lunches, bar lunches,
dinner dance Sat, no meals Sun, garden
A4 s'posted Reading, on L    ¼m

**12** **Old Lamb Motel, Theale** (Reading
**H2** 302357) Thatched, extension with 14
bedrms with bath, residents bar, dinner
19.00-22.00, closed Sun
A4 s'posted Theale, on loop road into
town, L at junction, on R    ¼m

**14** **Bear, Hungerford** (H. 2512)
**H3** Freehouse; old coaching house, **12
(R)** bedrms, restaurant, lunch 12.00-14.00
(exc Mon), dinner 19.00-21.30 (exc Sun
& Mon) t d'hote & a la c, bar meals
A338 s'posted Hungerford, R at A4,
on L    3m

**15** **Post House, Swindon** (S. 24601)
**H4** Trust House Forte; ***103 bedrms with
**(R)** bath & TV, foyer lounge, restaurant,
bkfst 07.30-10.30, lunches 12.30-14.00,
dinner 19.00-22.00, t d'hote & a la c,
bar, buttery with quick meals until 22.30
daily, heated swimming pool, bargain
break weekends, garden
A345 s'posted Swindon, R at 2nd r'bout
1m

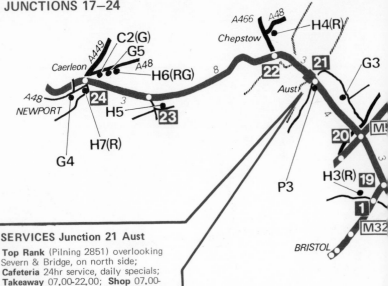

**Junction 18** for Bath, 18m. **Junction 19** M32 spur to Bristol, 4m. **Junction 20** Junction with M5 Birmingham – Exeter. **Severn Bridge** Toll; cars 12p, m/cycles 5p. Lorry weight limit 32 tons. Rush hour bottleneck; Midlands & North traffic should take M50 to Ross; then A40 & A449 to Junction 24 on M4. **Junction 22** for Chepstow Racecourse

## CAFES

**18**
**C1**
**(G)**
**Blue Star, Old Sodbury**
10.00-18.00 (08.00-18.00 summer weekends, closed Sun), chargeable o/n parking, Texaco petrol, 07.00-21.00 (10.00-18.00 Sun), limited spares
A46 s'posted Stroud, on L          2¾m

**24**
**C2**
**(G)**
**Taylors Cafe, Langstone**
05.30-21.00 (08.00-20.30 Sun), cooked meals, snacks, transport B&B, Esso petrol, derv, 05.30-21.00
A48 s'posted Langstone, on R          ¼m

## GARAGES

**17**
**G1**
**Corston Garage, Corston** (Malmesbury 3317) Amoco. Petrol, derv, AA rprs bkdn normal working hours, Ford age A429 s'posted Cirencester, on R

**17**
**G2**
**Priors Garage, Kington Langley**
Esso. 08.00-20.00 (09.00-17.00 Sun) petrol, 24hr bkdn, serv & rprs norma hours
A429 s'posted Chippenham, R by pic area at crossroads

**21**
**G3**
**Olveston Central Garage, Olveston** (Almondsbury 612266) National. 08.00-19.00 (08.00-18.00 Sat, closed Sun), petrol, AA bkdn, serv & rprs normal hours
A4461 s'posted Olveston, R fork int village

**24**
**G4**
**Treberth Service Station, Newport** (N. 45300) Esso. 07.00-23.00, petrol derv, spares, 24hr bkdn serv
A48 s'posted Newport

**24**
**G5**
**Hillcroft Garage, Langstone** (Llanwer 2040) 07.30-22.00 (09.00-22.00 Sun 24hr bkdn (Magor 521 night), serv & rprs normal hours, limited spares
A48 s'posted Langstone, through vill on R side

## PUBS

**18**
**P1**
**Dog, Old Sodbury** (Chipping Sodbur (312006) Whitbread; Cotswold stone character pub, lunches 12.00-14.00, dinner 19.00-22.00 (exc Sun & Mon garden
A46 s'posted Stroud, L at traffic lig in village

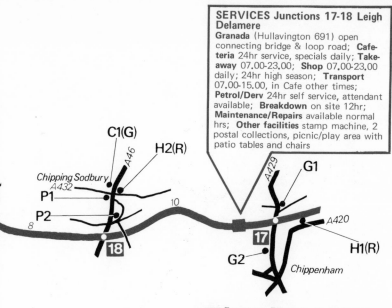

**SERVICES Junctions 17-18 Leigh Delamere**
**Granada** (Hullavington 691) open connecting bridge & loop road; **Cafeteria** 24hr service, specials daily; **Take-away** 07.00-23.00; **Shop** 07.00-23.00 daily; 24hr high season; **Transport** 07.00-15.00, in Cafe other times; **Petrol/Derv** 24hr self service, attendant available; **Breakdown** on site 12hr; **Maintenance/Repairs** available normal hrs; **Other facilities** stamp machine, 2 postal collections, picnic/play area with patio tables and chairs

**19**
**M32/1**
H3 (R)
**Eurocrest, Filton** (Bristol 564242)
Bass; **** 151 bedrms with bath & TV, lounge, restaurant, bkfst 07.00-10.00, lunch 12.30-14.00, dinner 19.00-22.00, t d'hote & a la c, buffet, Sunday lunch, bar snacks, dinner dance Thurs, Fri & Sat, bargain weekends, garden, terrace
M32 s'posted Bristol, turn off at Junction 1 s'posted Filton ¼m

**22**
H4 (R)
**Two Rivers Hotel,** Chepstow (C.5151)
Freehouse; *** 28 bedrms with bath or shower & TV, lounge, restaurant, bkfst 07.30-09.15, lunch 12.00-14.15, t d'hote & a la c, dinner 19.00-22.00 (exc Sun) a la c, mainly grills, Sunday lunch, bar meals, live music Thurs, Fri & Sat, sauna, solarium
A466 s'posted Chepstow, R on A48 in town, on L 1½m

**23**
H5
**Magor Court, Magor** (M. 457)
6 rooms B&B, evening meal on request, lounge, garden
B4245 s'posted Magor, on L in village 1m

**24**
H6 (R) (G)
**New Inn Hotel, Langstone** (Llanwern 2426) Ansells; roadside pub with motel annexe, 30 bedrms with shower. TV lounge, restaurant, bkfst 07.00-09.30, lunch 12.00-14.30, dinner 19.00-22.15, t d'hote & a la c, Sunday lunch, bar meals, garden, BP petrol 24hr
A48 s'posted Langstone, in village 1½m

**24**
H7 (R)
**Gateway Hotel, Newport** (Llanwern 2777) Freehouse; *** 90 bedrms with bath & TV, lounge, restaurant, bkfst 07.15-09.30, lunch 12.15-14.15 t d'hote, dinner 19.00-22.00, t d'hote & a la c, Sunday lunch, coffee shop 09.00-21.00, coaches welcome, garden
A48 s'posted Newport, on L ¼m

**18**
P2
**Compass Inn, Tormarton** (Badminton 242)
Freehouse; enlarged country pub with naval knick-knacks, 5 rooms B&B, residents lounge, lunches, dinners, seafood bar snacks, garden
A46 s'posted Stroud, R at 1st junction ½m

**21**
P3
**Boars Head, Aust** (Pilning 2278)
Courage; 17C coaching stage, lunch 12.00-14.00, light evening meals 19.00-21.30 (exc Sun), trad ale, garden, caravan site
A403 s'posted Avonmouth, L onto B4461 ½m

## HOTELS

**7**
11 (R)
**Bell Hotel, Sutton Benger** (Seagry 720401)
Freehouse; enlarged old pub, full of character, 15 bedrms with bath & TV, gourmet restaurant, bkfst 08.00-10.00, lunch 12.30-14.00, dinner 19.30-22.00, garden
A429 s'posted Chippenham, R on minor road s'posted Sutton Benger 2½m

**8**
12 (R)
**Cross Hands Hotel, Old Sodbury** (Chipping Sodbury 313000) Freehouse; character coaching house, ** 15 bedrms, some with bath, lounge, 2 restaurants, lunch 12.00-14.00, dinner 18.30-22.30 (18.30-23.00 Sat) t d'hote & a la c, mainly grills, garden
A46 s'posted Stroud, at crossroads 2¼m

# M4. JUNCTIONS 25–49 Part only open

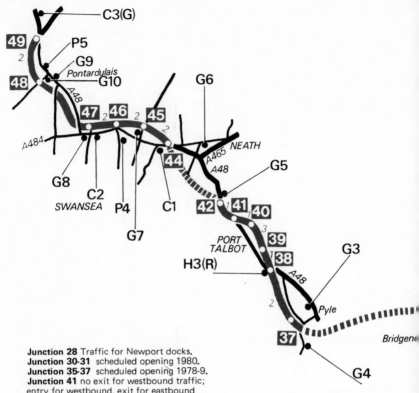

**Junction 28** Traffic for Newport docks.
**Junction 30-31** scheduled opening 1980.
**Junction 35-37** scheduled opening 1978-9.
**Junction 41** no exit for westbound traffic; entry for westbound, exit for eastbound traffic. **Junction 42** End of A48M.
**Junction 46** No entry for westbound traffic, no exit for eastbound traffic.
**Junction 49** End of M, Carmarthen 20m NW

## CAFES

**44** **Bamboo Cafe, Llansamlet**
**C1** 07.00-18.00 snacks and set lunches, closed Sun
A48 s'posted Swansea, through village
½m

**47** **Midway Cafe, Gorseinon**
**C2** 08.00-18.00 (08.00-12.00 Sat, closed Sun), bkfst, special lunches, snacks, o/n parking
L onto A48, on R
¼m

**49** **Maes Cafe, Cwmgwile** (Cross Hand 642326)
**C3** 08.30-20.30, cooked meals and snacks in small cafe, Esso petrol, derv, 08.30-
**(G)** 22.00, bkdn, serv & rprs
On A48 at W end of Motorway on R 2m

## HOTELS

**Mercury Hotel, Castleton** (C. 591)
Freehouse; ** 55 bedrm with bath & T
**H1** foyer lounge, restaurant, bkfst 07.30-
**(R)** 09.30, lunch 12.00-14.00, dinner 19.00-
21.00, a la c & t d'hote, garden
A48 s'posted Cardiff, on R 2½

**Post House, Pentwyn** (Cardiff 750121)
Trust House Forte; ***150 bedrm with
**H2** bath & TV, lounge, restaurant, bkfst
**(R)** 07.00-10.30, lunch 12.30-14.15, t d'hot
& a la c, dinner 19.00-22.30, a la c,
Sunday lunch, buttery for quick meals,
bar meals, garden
M extn, A48 loop road s'posted Cardiff
then to Pentwyn turn-off ¾

**Twelve Knights Hotel, Margam** (Port Talbot 2381) Freehouse; red brick
**H3** hotel, 11 bedrm with bath & TV,
**(R)** restaurant, carvery morning & evening,
12.30-14.30, 19.30-22.30, bar lunches
A4211 s'posted Port Talbot, on L ¾

## PUBS

**26 P1** **Three Blackbirds, Llantarnam** (Cwmbran 3130) Ind Coope; pretty pub, lunches 12.00-14.00, dinner 19.00-21.30
A4042 s'posted Abergavenny, through Malpas, in village          3m

**28 P2 (R)** **Tredegar Arms, Bassaleg**
Whitbread; village pub on the old road
A4072 s'posted Caerphilly, at junction with A468          ½m

**28 P3** **Stonehouse, St Brides** (Newport 65823)
Freehouse; private house converted to pub, lunches 12.00-14.30, dinner 19.00-22.00, a la c, Sunday lunch, beer garden
A48 s'posted Newport at junction with B4239          ½m

**46 P4** **Plough and Harrow, Llangyfelach** (Swansea 71816) Courage; ex-farmhouse, lunches 12.00-14.00 Mon-Fri, restaurant, bar meals, garden
B4489 s'posted Swansea (westbound exit only)          ½m

**49 P5** **Bird in Hand, Fforest** (Swansea 882466) Freehouse; 17C farmhouse, bar lunches 12.30-14.00, restaurant 19.00-22.30 Sat
A48 s'posted Pontardulais, through village          ¾m

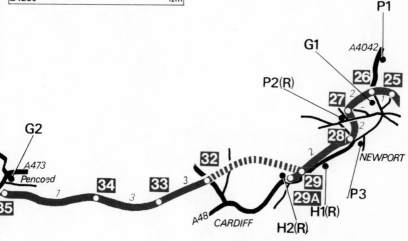

## GARAGES

**James Emmanuel Filling Station, Newport**
**G1** Shell. 07.00-23.00 (08.00-22.00 Sun), petrol, derv
S on A4042 s'posted Newport, on R ¼m

**Riverside Filling Station, Pencoed**
BP. 07.00-21.00 (08.00-21.00 Sun),
**G2** petrol, derv
A473 s'posted Pencoed          1m

**R. T. Clark, Pyle** (Kenfig Hill 740322)
Gulf. 08.00-20.00 (closed Sun), petrol,
**G3** bkdn, serv & rprs normal hours, Leyland agent, Unipart spares
A48 s'posted Pyle, in village          ¾m

**Globe Garage, Newton** (Porthcawl 2067)
Petrol, AA ** serv & rprs, AA bkdn
**G4** (Porthcawl 3616 night)
A4283 s'posted Porthcawl, L s'posted Newton          2½m

**Pine Tree Service, Briton Ferry** (BF 2360)
Shell. 07.30-21.00 (09.00-21.00 Sun),
**G5** petrol, bkdn, serv & rprs normal hours
A48 s'posted Neath, on L          ½m

**Longlas, Skewan** (Swansea 812425)
Texaco. 08.00-22.00 (09.00-21.00 Sun),
**G6** petrol, derv, 24hr bkdn, serv & rprs normal hours, limited spares
A48 s'posted Neath, L to Skewan          ¼m

**Glencollen Service Station, Glencollen** (Swansea 74418) 08.00-19.30 (10.00-
**G7** 17.00 Sun), petrol, 24hr bkdn (Swansea 794909 night), serv & rprs normal hours
A4067 s'posted Swansea, by roundabout          ¼m

**Cross Garage, Pentless Gaer** (Swansea 892819) Jet. 07.00-22.00 (09.00-21.00
**G8** Sun), petrol, 24hr bkdn, serv & rprs normal hours
A48 s'posted Carmarthen          ¼m

**Walters Garage, Pontardulais** (P.882238)
BP. 07.00-21.00, petrol, derv, bkdn, serv
**G9** & rprs normal hours, limited spares
A4138 s'posted Pontardulais, to junction with A48          ¾m

**Hendy Services, Hendy** (Swansea 882679)
BP. 08.00-20.00, petrol, 24hr bkdn, RAC
**G10** recovery agent, serv & rprs normal hours, Unipart spares
A4138 s'posted Pontardulais, on R          ½m

# M5. Birmingham-Exeter

JUNCTIONS 1 – 7

**Interchange M5/M6** Start of M5, Junction 8 M6, no exit. **Junction 4** Proposed Intersection for end of M42 Birmingham-Nottingham Motorway. **Junction 6/7** Worcester to west, Evesham 13m east

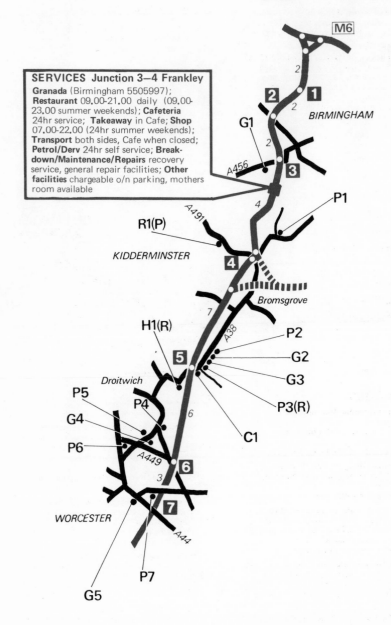

SERVICES Junction 3–4 Frankley
**Granada** (Birmingham 5505997); **Restaurant** 09.00-21.00 daily (09.00-23.00 summer weekends); **Cafeteria** 24hr service; **Takeaway** in Cafe; **Shop** 07.00-22.00 (24hr summer weekends); **Transport** both sides, Cafe when closed; **Petrol/Derv** 24hr self service; **Breakdown/Maintenance/Repairs** recovery service, general repair facilities; **Other facilities** chargeable o/n parking, mothers room available

M6

2

2 1

BIRMINGHAM

G1

2

A456

3

4

P1

A491

R1(P)

KIDDERMINSTER

4

7

Bromsgrove

A38

P2

H1(R)

5

G2

G3

P3(R)

Droitwich

P5

P4

C1

G4

6

P6

A449

3

6

7

WORCESTER

A44

P7

G5

## CAFES

**5**
**C1**
**Sunnyside Cafe, Wychbold**
07.30-17.00 Mon-Fri, lunches,
cooked meals, snacks
A38 s'posted Bromsgrove, on L          ¼m

## GARAGES

**3**
**G1**
**Heron, Halesowen**
Mobil. Petrol self serve, rprs & serv
A456 s'posted Kidderminster, on L     ¾m

**5**
**G2**
**Forge Garage, Wychbold** (W.205)
Esso. 07.00-21.30, petrol, derv, AA
bkdn (night W.475), gen serv & rprs
08.30-18.30 (including Sun am)
A38 s'posted Bromsgrove, on L        ½m

**5**
**G3**
**Wychbold Garage, Wychbold** (W.448)
National. 08.30-19.00, petrol, AA bkdn,
(Droitwich 3911 night) serv & rprs
normal hours
A38 s'posted Bromsgrove, on R       ½m

**6**
**G4**
**Claines Service Station, Fernhill Heath**
Shell. Petrol, 24hr bkdn (Worcester 27298)
A448 s'posted Worcester, R at junction,
R onto A38                          1½m

**7**
**G5**
**Redhill Service Station** (Worcester
353777) Shell. Petrol, 24hr note-
operated self serv, bkdn normal hours
(Worcester 356520 night)
A44 s'posted Worcester at junction with
A422                                ¾m

## PUBS

**4**
**P1**
**Plough, Rubery**
Ansells; large pub, steak bar
A38 s'posted Birmingham             2m

**5**
**P2**
**Swan, Upper Warren** (Wychbold 213)
Davenport; tudor front, bar snacks, trad
beer, lawns
A38 s'posted Bromsgrove             1m

**5**
**P3**
**(R)**
**Crown, Wychbold** (W.413)
Wolverhampton; mock tudor, 7 rms
B&B, restaurant, lunch 12.00-14.00,
dinner 19.00-21.30 (closed Sun), bar
meals
A38 s'posted Bromsgrove, on L       ½m

**6**
**P4**
**Swan, Martin Hussingtree** (Worcester
51364) Marstons; old farmhouse, lunchtime bar meals, evening snacks, trad beer,
garden
A4538 s'posted Droitwich to A38, on R
1¼m

**6**
**P5**
**White Hart, Fernhill Heath** (Worcester
51223) Davenport; old coaching house,
lunches, evening meals, mainly grills, trad
beer
A449 s'posted Worcester, R at junction,
R on to A38                         1¾m

**6**
**P6**
**Mug House, Claines**
Small village pub in churchyard, good
bar snacks
A449 s'posted Worcester, L to Claines,
by church                           2½m

**7**
**P7**
**Swan, Whittington** (Worcester 354892)
Banks; ex-manor house, character pub,
bar lunches Mon-Fri, rolls Sat, trad beer,
garden
A44 s'posted Worcester. R on A422   ¼m

## RESTAURANTS

**4**
**R1**
**(P)**
**Bell, Bell End** (Belbroughton 730232)
Mitchell & Butler; old country pub,
rebuilt, mainly restaurant trade, daily
t'd'hote lunches, extensive a la c
lunches & dinners, closed Sun evening,
last orders 13.45 & 22.30, garden
A491 s'posted Stourbridge, at junction
A4188                               2m

## HOTELS

**5**
**H1**
**(R)**
**Chateau Impney, Droitwich** (D. 4411)
Freehouse; romantic, exclusive, ★★★★65
bedrms with bath, restaurant, gourmet
menu lunchtime & evening, bar, gardens
A38, s'posted Droitwich, on L, off road
½m

# M5. JUNCTIONS 8 – 9
## M50 Ross Spur

SERVICES Junction 7-8 Strensham
**Kenning Motor Group** (Tewkesbury 293004); **Cafeteria** 24hr service; **Take-away** in Cafe; **Shop** 08.00-22.00; **Transport** 24hr service (closed Sat); **Petrol/Derv** 24hr self service; **Breakdown/Maintenance/Repairs** repairs & spares on site, bkdn 24hr service; **Other facilities** chargeable o/n parking. **Pub** Cavalier, freehouse serving substantial bar meals (exc Tues evening) and trad ale, with garden, is 5 mins walk from service area on northbound carriageway in Strensham village

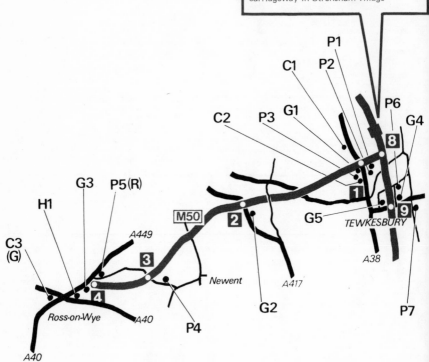

## CAFES

**50 1 C1** **Old Hut Cafe, Stratton**
Small transport cafe, 07.00-17.00
Mon-Fri
A38 s'posted Worcester on L          1m

**50 1 C2** **Joe's Cafe, Twyning**
Transport mainly, 06.30-19.00 Mon-Fri,
06.30-21.00 Sat, closed Sun, accommodation Mon-Fri (transport only)
S on A38 s'posted Tewkesbury, on L
                                    1½m

**50 4 C3 (G)** **Cross Road Cafeteria, Ross-on-Wye**
07.30-21.00, full meals & snacks
Garage: Kenning Motor Group, Texaco,
petrol & derv, 24hr self serv, bkdn &
recovery (Shrewsbury 52444)
On A449, at r'bout on W side          1½m

## GARAGES

**50 1 G1** **Twyning Service Station, Twyning**
(Tewkesbury 294212) Texaco. 08.00-
21.00, petrol, derv, serv & emergency rprs,
light local recovery, private get you home
service, small shop, o/n parking for 2
caravans
A38 s'posted Tewkesbury, on R          1½m

**50 2 32** **Bromsberrow Filling Station**
(Bromsberrow 296) 07.30-19.00 Mon-Sat,
(09.00-13.00 Sun), petrol, small shop
A417 s'posted Gloucester, on L          ¼m

**50 4 ;3** **Spur Filling Station, Ross-on-Wye**
BP. 07.00-21.00 (07.00-23.00 high
summer), weekends 08.00-21.00, petrol,
derv
A449 s'posted Monmouth, on R          ¼m

**9 ;4** **Ashchurch Filling Station, Ashchurch**
07.00-22.00 (09.00-21.00 Sun), petrol,
derv, shop
A438 s'posted Evesham, on R          ¼m

**9 ;5** **Graham Wright Motors, Tewkesbury**
(T. 292398) 07.00-18.00, petrol, derv,
serv & rprs normal hours, Ford & Vauxhall agent
A438 s'posted Tewkesbury, on R          ½m

## PUBS

**50 1 ,1** **Village Inn, Twyning Green**
Whitbread; picturesque pub on village
green, trad beer, pies only
L at 1st exit (not A38) to village ← on
green                                    1m

**50 1 ,2** **Fleet, Twyning Green** (Tewkesbury
292563) Whitbread; riverside pub, book
for full meals, bar snacks, trad beer,
garden, own moorings on River Avon
L at 1st exit (not A38) to green, R side
of green to river          1m

**50 1 ,3** **Crown, Twyning**
Ind Coope; small family pub, good bar
snacks, garden
A38 s'posted Tewkesbury, on R          1½m

**50 3 ,4** **Roadmaker, Gorsley** (G. 352)
Whitbread; old pub, bar meals, trad
beer, gardens, swings
B4221 s'posted Newent, on R          ½m

**M50 4 P5 (R)** **Travellers Rest, Ross-on-Wye**
(R-o-W 3861) Whitbread; modern pub,
basically a steak house, fair choice of
fixed price grills, lunch & supper extension,
garden
W end of Motorway r'bout          ¼m

**9 P6** **Northway, Northway** (Tewkesbury
294277) Ind Coope; old victorian house
in own grounds, 3 rooms B&B, bar meals
& snacks, trad beer
A438 s'posted Evesham, L into village
on L          ½m

**9 P7** **Queens Head, Ashchurch** (Brendon 72440)
Whitbread; small pub, light bar meals
day & evenings, skittle alley, garden
A438 s'posted Evesham, on R at crossroads          1½m

## HOTELS

**M50 4 H1** **Wilton House Hotel, Ross-on-Wye**
(R-o-W 2234) Georgian manor house
in own grounds, 10 rooms B&B
On A449 s'posted Monmouth at r'bout
on L          1½m

# M5. JUNCTIONS 10 – 16

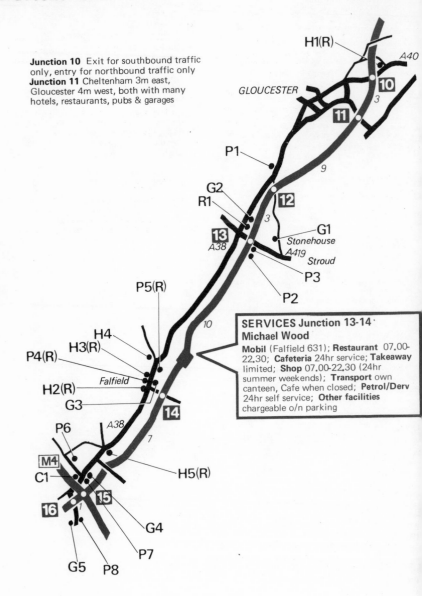

**Junction 10** Exit for southbound traffic only, entry for northbound traffic only
**Junction 11** Cheltenham 3m east, Gloucester 4m west, both with many hotels, restaurants, pubs & garages

H1(R)

A40

GLOUCESTER

10

11

3

P1

9

G2

R1

12

3

13

A38

G1

Stonehouse

A419

Stroud

P3

P2

P5(R)

10

H4

H3(R)

P4(R)

Falfield

H2(R)

G3

14

**SERVICES Junction 13-14**
**Michael Wood**

**Mobil** (Falfield 631); **Restaurant** 07.00-22.30; **Cafeteria** 24hr service; **Takeaway** limited; **Shop** 07.00-22.30 (24hr summer weekends); **Transport** own canteen, Cafe when closed; **Petrol/Derv** 24hr self service; **Other facilities** chargeable o/n parking

P6

A38

7

M4

C1

H5(R)

16

15

G4

P7

G5   P8

## CAFES

**16 C1** **Rocklands Cafe, Almondsbury**
(A. 612208) Small cafe with 2 rooms
B&B with TV, 10.00-18.00 lunches,
high teas, 19.30-21.30 set dinners, home
cooking, closed Mon
A38 s'posted Thornbury, on L     ½m

## GARAGES

**13 G1** **Newton Garage, Stonehouse** (S. 2180)
Ken Weaver's 24hr bkdn serv, rprs &
serv normal hours, 24hr call out
A419 s'posted Stroud, L on A4008     ½m

**13 G2** **Old Forge Filling Station, Whitminster**
Esso. 24hr self serv prepayment petrol/
derv
To A38, R,on L     ½m

**14 G3** **Falfield Garage, Falfield** (F. 286)
Esso. Petrol, bkdn, serv & rprs
To A38, R,on R     ½m

**16 G4** **Almondsbury Filling Station,
Almondsbury** BP. 07.00-21.00
(09.00-21.00 Sun), petrol,serv & rprs
Mon-Fri
A38 s'posted Thornbury, on R     1m

**16 G5** **Stoke Brook Service Station, Patchway**
Esso. 07.00-21.00 Mon-Fri, serv & rprs
A38 s'posted Bristol, on R     1½m

## PUBS

**12 P1** **Cross Keys, Hardwick** (H. 216)
Whitbread; old Cotswold pub, bar meals,
trad beer, garden
A38 s'posted Gloucester, on L     ¾m

**13 P2** **Kings Head, Eastington**
(Stonehouse 2934) Whitbread; Georgian
village pub, 2 rooms B&B, snacks,
garden
A419 s'posted Stroud, 1st R to village,
on junction     1½m

**13 P3** **Victoria, Eastington** (Stonehouse
2892) Whitbread; cosy Cotswold pub,
comprehensive bar meals, lunch & evening
meals, garden, skittle alley, coaches
welcome
A419 s'posted Stroud, 1st R to village,
on L     1½m

**14 P4 (R)** **Huntsman House, Falfield** (F. 239)
Whitbread; small village pub, bar meals,
snacks, restaurant, plain lunches, cold
buffet & limited a la c evenings, garden
To A38,R,on L     ⅓ m

**14 P5 (R)** **Berkeley Vale, Stone** (Falfield 219)
Ex-private house, B&B, dining room,
bar meals, snacks, trad beer, garden
To A38, R,on R     1¼m

**16 P6** **Swan, Tockington** (Almondsbury
614800) Courage; olde worlde, bar
meals, snacks, garden, seats outside
A38 s'posted Thornbury, L into Tockington, R fork in village     2½m

**16 P7** **Swan, Almondsbury**
Courage; coaching house, 3 rooms B&B,
light lunches & evening snacks
A38 s'posted Thornbury, on R     ¼m

**16 P8** **New Inn, Patchway** (Almondsbury
612238) Courage; modernised coach
house with stables as diningroom,lunches
& dinners a la c (exc Sun & Mon), bar
meals, mainly home cooking, garden
A38 s'posted Bristol, on L     ¼m

## RESTAURANTS

**13 R1** **Old Forge, Whitminster** (Saul 875)
Tudor smithy, lunch a la c & t d'hote,
last orders 14.00, full a la c evening
meals, last orders 23.00, closed Mon
To A38, R,on R     ½m

## HOTELS

**11 H1 (R)** **Golden Valley Hotel, Cheltenham**
(C. 32691) Freehouse; ****103 rooms
with TV & bath, restaurant, bkfst
07.30-09.30, lunch 12.00-14.15, dinner
19.00-21.30, t d'hote & a la c, bar meals,
garden
A40 s'posted Cheltenham, on L at r'bout
1½m

**14 H2 (R)** **Park Hotel, Falfield** (F. 550)
Freehouse; Georgian house in own
grounds, 10 rooms B&B, garden, full
t d'hote & a la c, closed Sun evening
To A38, L,on L     1m

**14 H3 (R)** **Gables Hotel, Falfield** (F. 272)
Freehouse; converted private house,
B&B, bar meals, restaurant a la c,
mainly grills, afternoon teas and snacks,
garden
To A38, R,on L     ⅓m

**14 H4** **Elms, Stone** (Falfield 279)
17C farmhouse,12 rooms B&B, dinner,
garden
To A3, R, L through village, on L     1½m

**16 H5 (R)** **Post House, Alveston** (Thornbury 412521)
Trust House Forte; ***75 rooms with
bath, restaurant, bkfst 07.15-09.30,
lunch 12.00-14.00, dinner 19.00-21.30,
t d'hote & a la c, garden
A38 s'posted Thornbury, in village     2¾m

# M5. JUNCTIONS 17 – 22

**Junction 22** A38 s'posted Bristol Airport for Cheddar Gorge

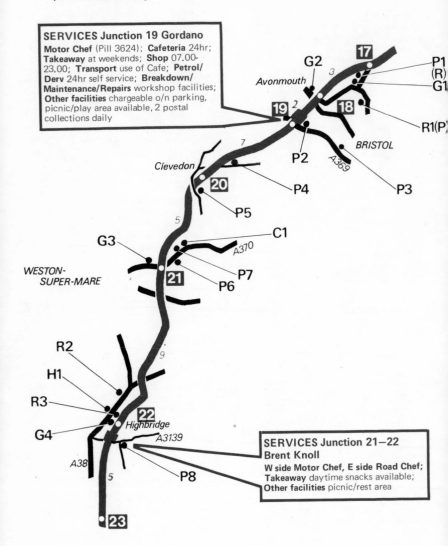

**SERVICES Junction 19 Gordano**
**Motor Chef** (Pill 3624); **Cafeteria** 24hr; **Takeaway** at weekends; **Shop** 07.00-23.00; **Transport** use of Cafe; **Petrol/Derv** 24hr self service; **Breakdown/Maintenance/Repairs** workshop facilities; **Other facilities** chargeable o/n parking, picnic/play area available, 2 postal collections daily

**SERVICES Junction 21–22 Brent Knoll**
**W side Motor Chef, E side Road Chef; Takeaway** daytime snacks available; **Other facilities** picnic/rest area

## CAFES

**21** **Hewish Cafeteria, Hewish**
Self service meals & snacks
**C1** A370 s'posted Bristol, on L      2m

## GARAGES

**17** **Cribbs Causeway Filling Station**
Shell. 24hr self serv petrol
**G1** A4018 s'posted Bristol, on R      ½m

**18** **Avonmouth Filling Station, Avonmouth**
BP. 07.15-22.00 (09.00-18.00 Sat & Sun)
**G2** self serv petrol
A4 s'posted Avonmouth      ½m

**21** **Weston Motoring Centre**
National. 07.00-22.00 self serv petrol,
**G3** tyre, exhaust & brake serv 08.30-18.00
(09.00-13.00 Sun)
A370 s'posted Weston, on R      1m

**22** **Brent Knoll Garage, Brent Knoll**
(BK. 248) 08.00-18.00 petrol, rprs,
**G4** AA serv
A38 s'posted Bristol Airport, on R    ½m

## PUBS

**17** **Lamb & Flag, Cribbs Causeway**
(Bristol 501490) Courage; old farm-
**P1** house, now busy pub, bar meals & snacks,
**(R)** businessmans lunch & dinner, a la c
Mon-Fri, buffet Sat & Sun, garden,
coaches welcome
A4018 s'posted Bristol, on R      ¼m

**19** **Kings Arms, Easton-in-Gordano** (Pill
2208) Courage; friendly village pub,
**P2** lunches, bar meals, snacks in evening,
trad beer, skittle alley, garden
A369 s'posted Clifton, L s'posted Pill
     ½m

**19** **George, Abbotsleigh** (Pill 2467)
Courage; popular pub, substantial bar
**P3** snacks, trad beer
A369 s'posted Clifton, on R at Xroads
     1¾m

**20** **Star, Tickenham** (Nailsea 2071)
Courage; old pub in attractive setting,
**P4** 3 rooms, B&B, lunches, bar meals,
garden
B3133 s'posted Clevedon, R to town,
B3130 s'posted Nailsea on L      2½m

**20** **Drum and Monkey, Kenn** (Clevedon 3433)
Courage; old character pub, lunches, bar
**P5** snacks
B3133 s'posted Clevedon, L, over
Motorway towards Kenn, on L      1½m

**21** **Palmers Elm Inn, Hewish** (Yatton
832245) Watneys; 19C coaching stop,
**P6** 3 rooms B&B, grills & bar snacks,
impromptu live music on organ
A370 s'posted Bristol, on R      1m

**21** **Full Quart, Hewish** (Yatton
833077) Freehouse; basket meals,
**P7** snacks available, childrens garden
A370 s'posted Bristol, on L      2m

**22** **Watchfield Inn, Watchfield**
Whitbread; small village pub, light
**P8** lunches & snacks, caravan & camping
site, skittle alley
A38 s'posted Highbridge, L in ½m
onto B3139, R onto B3141, on green
     2m

## RESTAURANTS

**17** **Old Crow, Brentry** (Bristol 501343)
Watneys; busy roadside pub, bar meals
**R1** & snacks, children's area, primarily a
**(P)** restaurant, weekday businessmans lunch,
Sat & Sun lunch, dinners a la c (exc Sun
evenings)
A4018 s'posted Bristol, past r'bout, on
R      1½m

**22** **Greystone, Brent Knoll** (BK. 239)
Old beamed cottage, lunch (last orders
**R2** 13.45), Sunday lunch, dinners (last
orders 22.15) a la c, closed Sun evening,
Mon & Tue, booking advisable for evening
meals
A38 s'posted Bristol Airport, on R    ¼m

**22** **Brent House, East Brent** (BK.246/500)
Victorian interior, dinner dances to live
**R3** music, Mon-Sat, lunches until 14.00,
Sunday lunch, other meals extensive a la c,
good wine selection, swimming pool, sauna
& solarium, closed Sun evenings and some
Mons off season
A38 s'posted Bristol Airport, on L    2m

## HOTELS

**22** **Battleborough Grange, Brent Knoll**
(BK.208) Small country residential
**H1** hotel in own grounds, 12 rooms B&B,
dinner, family cooking, TV lounge
A38 s'posted Bristol Airport, on L    ½m

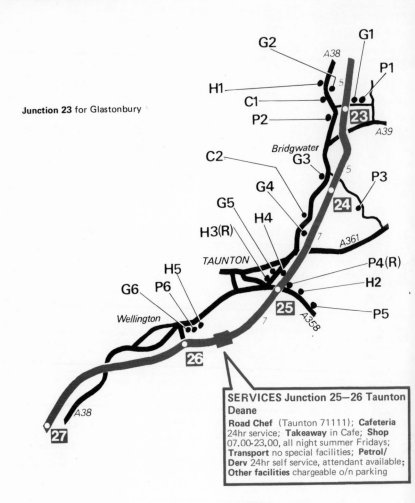

Junction 23 for Glastonbury

G2
G1
H1
P1
C1
P2
A38
5
C2
Bridgwater
G3
G4
23
A39
G5
H4
H3(R)
5
P3
TAUNTON
24
H5
P4(R)
G6
P6
H2
7
A361
Wellington
25
P5
7
A358
26
A38
27

SERVICES Junction 25–26 Taunton
Deane
**Road Chef** (Taunton 71111); **Cafeteria**
24hr service; **Takeaway** in Cafe; **Shop**
07.00-23.00, all night summer Fridays;
**Transport** no special facilities; **Petrol/
Derv** 24hr self service, attendant available;
**Other facilities** chargeable o/n parking

## CAFES

**23**
**C1** **Little Elm Tree Cafe, Pawlett** (Puriton 683308) 08.00-20.00, all meals, quick snacks, full menu, caravan accommodation available, no heavy transport
A38 s'posted Highbridge, on R     1½m

**24**
**C2** **Grahams Transport Stop, North Petherton** (NP. 662271) 06.00-22.00 Mon-Fri (06.00-12.00 Sat, closed Sun), lunches, full meals, snacks, o/n parking for sleeper lorries
A38 s'posted Taunton, on L     ¼m

## GARAGES

**23**
**G1** **Puriton Garage, Woolavington Rd, Puriton** (P. 683280) 07.00-19.00 (exc Sun) Petrol, bkdn, serv & rprs
A39 s'posted Glastonbury, L through village, on R     ½m

**23**
**G2** **Pawlett Service Station** (Bridgwater 683216) Jet. 06.00-23.00, petrol, bkdn, rprs
A38 s'posted Highbridge, on L     2m

**24**
**G3** **Westway Service Station, Bridgwater** (B. 3010) Mobil. Petrol 24hr, serv & rprs 08.30-17.30 Mon-Fri, Opel agent
A38 s'posted Bridgwater, on L     1½m

**24**
**G4** **Heathfield Garage, North Petherton** (NP. 662230) 07.30-20.30 (09.00-20.00 Sun), petrol, bkdn 24hr, serv & rprs 08.30-17.30 Mon-Fri
A38 s'posted Taunton, on R     ¾m

**25**
**G5** **Central Service Station, Bathpool** (Taunton 3587) Esso 05.00-20.00 (06.00-18.00 weekends), petrol, bkdn, serv & rprs normal hours
A38 s'posted Bridgwater, on R     ¼m

**26**
**G6** **Chelston Motors, Chelston** (Wellington 2075) Jet. 07.00-20.00, petrol, derv, bkdn, serv & rprs normal hours
A38 s'posted Taunton, on R     ½m

## PUBS

**23**
**P1** **Puriton Inn, Puriton** (Bridgwater 683464) Whitbreads; Victorian village pub, lunches, evening meals, home cooking, grills (exc Mon evening) skittle alley, bar games
A39 s'posted Glastonbury, L & L again to village, on L     ¼m

**23**
**P2** **Henry Fielding, Dumball** (Puriton 683308) Whitbread; 3 rooms B&B, lunches (exc Sun), bar snacks & meals, live entertainment Sun evening, fishing in King Sedge Drain
A38 s'posted Bridgwater, on L     ½m

**24**
**P3** **Thatchers Arms, Moorland** Whitbread; small attractive pub on River Parrett, snacks, skittle alley, garden
Minor road to Huntworth, R at fork     2½m

**25**
**P4**
**(R)** **Blackbrook, Ruishton** (Henlade 442245) Watneys; character pub, restaurant, lunch 12.30-14.00, t d'hote & a la c, dinner 19.15-21.30, a la c, Sunday lunch, closed Sun evening & all day Mon, trad beer, garden
A358 s'posted Yeovil, on L     ¼m

**25**
**P5** **Nags Head, Thornfalcon** (Henlade 442258) Watneys; beamed bar, lunch 12.00-14.00 (exc Sun), snacks other times, garden
A358 s'posted Yeovil, through hamlet, on R     1½m

**26**
**P6** **Blackbird, West Buckland** Watneys; old fashioned country pub, snacks available, B&B
A38 s'posted Taunton, on L     ¾m

## HOTELS

**23**
**H1** **Manor Arms, Pawlett** (Bridgwater 683275) Bass; 10 rooms B&B, lunches, buffet, bar meals, good snacks in evening, live entertainment, several bars, caravan park & camp site, garden
A38 s'posted Highbridge, on L     2m

**25**
**H2** **Falcon Hotel, Henlade** (H. 442502) Converted private house, 12 bedrms, dinner by arrangement, garden
A358 s'posted Yeovil, on L     1m

**25**
**H3**
**(R)** **Creech Castle Hotel, Bathpool** (Taunton 3512) Ansells; old enlarged house in own grounds, ***22 bedrms with bath, lounge, restaurant, a la c meals, Sunday lunch, large bar, hot & cold buffet, garden
A358 s'posted Taunton, by r'bout     ¼m

**25**
**H4** **St Quinton Hotel, Bathpool** (Taunton 3016) Converted farmhouse, 5 rooms B&B, caravan & camping site, shop
A38 s'posted Bridgwater, on R at bridge     ½m

**26**
**H5** **Heatherton Grange, Bradford-on-Tone** (B-on-T 232) B&B, lunches & dinners, bar meals, live music, groups at weekends
A38 s'posted Taunton, on R     1m

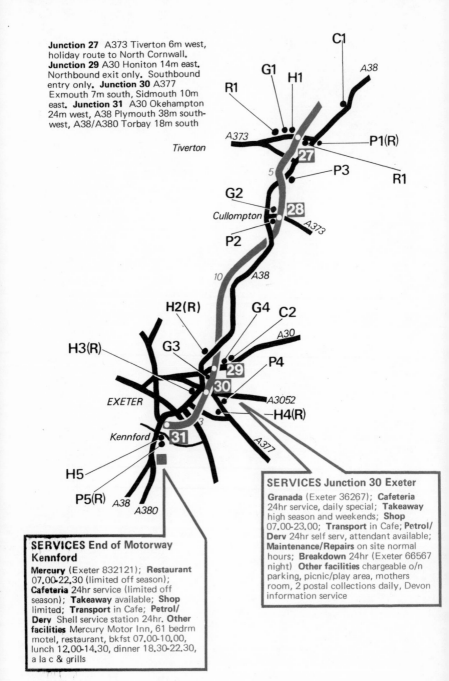

**Junction 27** A373 Tiverton 6m west, holiday route to North Cornwall. **Junction 29** A30 Honiton 14m east. Northbound exit only. Southbound entry only. **Junction 30** A377 Exmouth 7m south, Sidmouth 10m east. **Junction 31** A30 Okehampton 24m west, A38 Plymouth 38m south-west, A38/A380 Torbay 18m south

C1
A38
G1  H1
R1
A373
P1(R)
27
Tiverton
P3
5
R1
G2
28
Cullompton
A373
P2
10   A38
H2(R)
G4  C2
H3(R)
A30
G3
29
P4
30
EXETER
A3052
H4(R)
3
31
Kennford
A377
H5
P5(R)  A38  A380

### SERVICES Junction 30 Exeter

**Granada** (Exeter 36267); **Cafeteria** 24hr service, daily special; **Takeaway** high season and weekends; **Shop** 07.00-23.00; **Transport** in Cafe; **Petrol/Derv** 24hr self serv, attendant available; **Maintenance/Repairs** on site normal hours; **Breakdown** 24hr (Exeter 66567 night) **Other facilities** chargeable o/n parking, picnic/play area, mothers room, 2 postal collections daily, Devon information service

### SERVICES End of Motorway Kennford

**Mercury** (Exeter 832121); **Restaurant** 07.00-22.30 (limited off season); **Cafeteria** 24hr service (limited off season); **Takeaway** available; **Shop** limited; **Transport** in Cafe; **Petrol/Derv** Shell service station 24hr. **Other facilities** Mercury Motor Inn, 61 bedrm motel, restaurant, bkfst 07.00-10.00, lunch 12.00-14.30, dinner 18.30-22.30, a la c & grills

## CAFES

**27**
**C1** **Morgans Transport Cafe, Uffculme**
06.00-19.00 (06.00-22.00 Sat, closed Sun)
A38 s'posted Taunton, on L    2½m

**29**
**30**
**C2** **Black Horse, Clyst Honiton** (Exeter 67681) 05.45-23.00 (05.45-16.00 Sat) bkfst, lunch (until 14.00), chip meals, B&B for transport
N bound: J29 s'posted Honiton. S bound: J30, A38/30 s'posted Honiton    ½m

## GARAGES

**27**
**G1** **Kellands Garage, Sampford Peverell** (SP. 820264) Esso. 07.30-21.00, petrol, derv, bkdn & rprs normal hours, limited Sat, available Sun for call out
A373 s'posted Tiverton, on R in village    1m

**28**
**G2** **Whittons Service Station, Cullompton** Jet. 07.00-22.00, cut price petrol, bkdn 24hr serv, rprs 08.30-17.30 (08.30-13.00 Sat, closed Sun)
A373 s'posted Cullompton, on L    ¼m

**29**
**G3** **Standfield & White, Exeter** (E.68187) BP. 07.30-19.00 (09.30-18.00 Sun), petrol, bkdn serv, rprs normal hours, limited spares, Chrysler agent
A30 s'posted Exeter    ¼m

**29**
**30**
**G4** **Honiton Clyst Garage, Honiton Clyst** (Exeter 67235) 07.00-22.00 (08.00-21.00 Sun) petrol, derv, 24hr bkdn (Exeter 69849 night) serv & rprs normal hours
N bound: J29, A30 s'posted Honiton; S bound: J30, A38/30 s'posted Honiton    2½m

## PUBS

**27**
**P1**
**(R)** **Waterloo Inn, Waterloo Cross, Uffculme** (Craddock 317) Freehouse; restaurant, grills, home cooking, Sunday lunch, other meals a la c, bar meals, trad ale, camping & caravan site, accommodation, 2 caravans
A373 s'posted Taunton, at junction with A38    ¼m

**28**
**P2** **Showman, Cullompton** (C. 2317) Whitbread; Victorian pub, circus winter quarters at back of house, 3 rooms B&B, bar meals & snacks
A373 s'posted Cullompton, on L    200yds

**28**
**P3** **Verbeer Manor, Willand** (Cullompton 3312) Freehouse; 16C manor house, rambling bars, bar meals, buffet, garden, antique shop
A373 s'posted Cullompton, R onto A38    2½m

**30**
**P4** **Blue Ball, Clyst St Mary** Whitbread; old world pub, good home cooked meals
A3052 s'posted Sidmouth (dual carriage way, turn back at r'bout ¼m) L on A377 s'posted Exmouth    ¾m

**31**
**P5**
**(R)** **Gissons, Kennford** Freehouse; old converted farmhouse, restaurant, bar meals, garden
A38 s'posted Torbay, L on service road entrance    1m

## RESTAURANT

**27**
**R1** **Farmhouse Restaurant, Sampford Peverell** (SP. 20550) restaurant, lunches, dinners, bar, bar meals, bedrms with bath, garden
At r'bout by Junction 27    ¼m

## HOTELS

**27**
**H1** **Green Headlands Hotel, Sampford Peverell** (SP.820255) country hotel, 7 bedrms B&B, dinner, licensed bar. bkfsts, lunches, cream teas, dinners for non-residents, family cooking
A373 s'posted Tiverton, on R    1m

**29**
**30**
**H2**
**(R)** **Gipsy Hill Hotel, Pinhoe** (Exeter 65252) Freehouse; ***hotel in own grounds, 30 bedrms with bath, TV & residents lounge, restaurant, bkfst 07.45-09.30, lunch 12.30-14.00, dinner 19.30-21.00, a la c d'hote, Sunday lunch, bar meals, garden
N bound: J29, A38, R to Pinhoe, L at hilltop
S bound: J30, A38/A30 to Pinhoe, turn L at hilltop 1 m    2½m

**30**
**H3**
**(R)** **Crest Hotel, Exeter Bypass** (Exeter 35353) Bass; **58 bedrms, most with bath & TV, foyer lounge, restaurant, bkfst 07.30-09.30, dinner 19.00-21.30, t d'hote & a la c, mainly grills, bar snacks, garden
To service area, L at r'bout, on L    ½m

**30**
**H4**
**(R)**
**(P)** **George and Dragon, Clyst St George** (Topsham 4310) Bass; character pub, 8 bedrms, TV lounge, restaurant, bkfst 08.00-09.30, lunch 12.00-14.00, dinner 19.00-20.30 (21.30 weekends) t d'hote & a la c, Sunday lunch, closed Sun evenings, bar meals, trad beer, garden
A3052 s'posted Sidmouth, R on A377 s'posted Exmouth    2½m

**31**
**H5** **Fairwinds Hotel, Kennford** (Exeter 832911) Private; small family run hotel, 10 rooms B&B with TV, all meals t d'hote & a la c, bar
A38 s'posted Torbay, L at service road entrance    1m

# M6. M1 - Carlisle

JUNCTIONS 1–4 and M69
SPUR

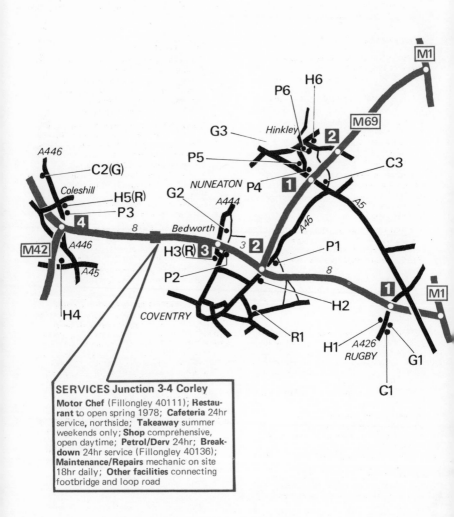

**SERVICES Junction 3-4 Corley**

**Motor Chef** (Fillongley 40111); **Restaurant** to open spring 1978; **Cafeteria** 24hr service, northside; **Takeaway** summer weekends only; **Shop** comprehensive, open daytime; **Petrol/Derv** 24hr; **Breakdown** 24hr service (Fillongley 40136); **Maintenance/Repairs** mechanic on site 18hr daily; **Other facilities** connecting footbridge and loop road

## CAFES

**1** **Glebe Cafe, Newbold**
**C1** 09.00-19.00 daily, salads, light meals, snacks
A426 s'posted Rugby, on L    2m

**4** **Grimstock Hill Cafe & Filling Station,**
**C2** Coleshill 08.00-17.00 Mon-Fri, meals
**(G)** & snacks. Shell (Coleshill 62190)
07.00-23.00, petrol, derv, AA bkdn serv
(night C. 63115), spares
A446 s'posted Lichfield, on L    1m

**M69** **Aviary Island, Burwash**
**1** 07.00-18.00 daily, meals & snacks
**C3** A5 s'posted Rugby, L at r'bout    ¼m

## GARAGES

**1** **Viaduct Service Station, Newbold**
**G1** (Rugby 74727) National. 08.00-21.00
(08.00-13.00 Sun), serv & rprs normal
hours, Toyota agency
A426 s'posted Rugby, on L    2m

**3** **Parkside Garage, Bedworth**
**G2** (Coventry 315631) Total; 07.30-20.00
(10.00-13.30 Sun), petrol, serv & rprs,
Leyland agent
A444 s'posted Nuneaton, R at r'bout on
to B4113, on L    1¼m

**M69** **County, Hinckley** (H. 37310)
**1** Petrol normal working hours, bkdn
**G3** until 22.00 (out of hours H.32476)
A5 s'posted Nuneaton, R s'posted
Hinckley, on L    ½m

## PUBS

**2** **Crown, Anstey**
**P1** Bass; 17C character pub, light meals
12.00-14.30 & 19.00-22.00
A46 s'posted Leicester, on old road to
village centre    ½m

**3** **Old Griffin, Longford** (Coventry 89120)
**P2** Small pub, B&B, bar and lounge meals
A444 s'posted Coventry, R by canal  ¼m

**4** **Coach Hotel, Coleshill**
**P3** Bass; Victorian house, B&B
A446 s'posted Lichfield, on L    1m

**M69** **Three Pots, Burbage** (Hinckley 32297)
**1** Bass; red brick roadside pub, lunch
**P4** daily (exc Sun), snacks at other times
A5 s'posted Nuneaton, at r'bout    ¼m

**M69** **Hinckley Knight, Burbage** (Hinckley
**1** 32335) Freehouse; popular crossroads
**P5** pub, lunches, steak bar, charcoal grill
(exc Sun)
A5 s'posted Nuneaton, beyond r'bout
¼m

**M69** **Union, Hinckley** (H. 37293)
**1** Country pub, B&B, lunches & dinners
**P6** A5 s'posted Nuneaton, R to town
centre    1½m

## RESTAURANTS

**2** **Vineyard, Binley** (Coventry 454159)
**R1** Modern restaurant, steak bars
A46 s'posted Coventry, L to A427    2m

## HOTELS

**1** **Brownsover Hall Hotel, Brownsover**
**H1** (Rugby 73138) Freehouse; built 1650 in
own grounds, 36 bedrms (some with bath/
shower), restaurant, bar, garden, caravan
site
A426 s'posted Rugby, R to village    ¼m

**2** **Eurocrest, Walsgrave** (W. 3261)
**H2** Bass; ***160 bedrms with TV & bath,
bkfst 07.00-09.30, lunch 12.00-14.30,
dinner 19.00-21.30, t d'hote & a la c,
Sunday lunch, cold & hot buffet, bar
lunches, sandwiches, shop, garden
A46 s'posted Coventry, on L    ¼m

**3** **Novotel, Longford** (Coventry 88833)
**H3** Freehouse; ***102 bedrms with TV &
**(R)** bath, 2 restaurants (1 for French
cuisine), 06.00-24.00, all meals, 2 bars,
dinner dance Fri & Sat, swimming pool,
6 squash courts, sauna, solarium,
gymnasium, special Sat terms for
accommodation & dinner dance, garden
At junction of loop road & A444 s'posted
Coventry    ¼m

**4** **Arden Motel, Hampton in Arden**
**H4** (H in A 2330) Private; 15 bedrms, lounge,
restaurant, bar, bar meals (mainly grills)
A446 s'posted Warwick, R on to A45,
on R    1¾m

**4** **Swan, Coleshill** (C. 62212)
**H5** Ansells; ** Georgian, 34 bedrm (most
**(R)** with TV & showers), restaurant, bkfst
07.00-09.00, lunch 12.30-14.00 a la c,
dinner 18.30-22.30 chefs speciality,
mainly grills, bar meals, buffet, Sunday
lunch
A446 s'posted Lichfield at crossroads 1m

**M69** **Vinery, Hinckley** (H. 36733)
**1** Freehouse; *17 bedrm (some with bath),
**H6** restaurant serving lunches & dinners
A5 s'posted Nuneaton, R to town centre
1½m

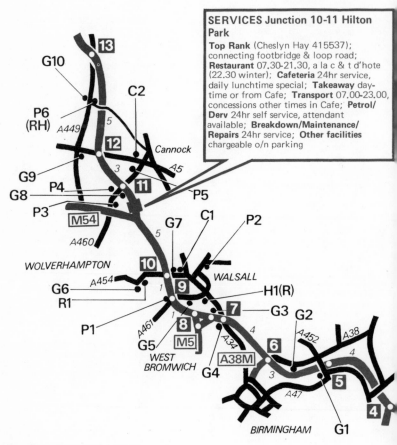

**SERVICES Junction 10-11 Hilton Park**
**Top Rank** (Cheslyn Hay 415537); connecting footbridge & loop road; **Restaurant** 07.30-21.30, a la c & t d'hote (22.30 winter); **Cafeteria** 24hr service, daily lunchtime special; **Takeaway** daytime or from Cafe; **Transport** 07.00-23.00, concessions other times in Cafe; **Petrol/Derv** 24hr self service, attendant available; **Breakdown/Maintenance/Repairs** 24hr service; **Other facilities** chargeable o/n parking

**Junction 6** Notorious Spaghetti Junction, A38M to Birmingham. **Junction 8** M5 Interchange only

## CAFES

**10** **Hills Cafe, Walsall**
**C1** 08.00-17.30 (08.00-23.00 Sat, closed
Sun) meals & snacks
A454 s'posted Walsall, on L ¼m

**12** **Hollies Transport Cafe, Wedges Mills**
**C2** 24hr, meals & snacks, accommodation
for transport drivers
A5 s'posted Cannock 1½m

## GARAGES

**5** **Clock Motors, Castle Bromwich**
**G1** (021-747-4712) BP. Petrol prepayment
24hr, serv & rprs normal hours,
Chrysler agent
To junction with A452 s'posted Sutton
Coldfield, on L ¼m

**6** **Petropolis Filling Station, Birmingham**
**G2** Total. 07.00-23.00 (08.00-22.00 Sun)
self serv petrol
A38 s'posted Lichfield, R onto B4148,
on R ½m

**7** **Tame Services, Great Barr** (021-357-7960)
**G3** National. 09.00-23.00 (08.00-23.00 week-
ends), petrol, bkdn & rprs normal hours
A34 s'posted Walsall, on L ¼m

**7** **Great Barr Garage, Great Barr**
**G4** BP. Petrol 24hr prepayment, serv & rprs
normal hours
A34 s'posted Birmingham, at r'bout ¼m

**9** **Walsall Way Services, Walsall** (W.25372)
**G5** National. 07.30-22.00 (09.00-22.00 Sun)
AA bkdn (021-743-8781 night) serv &
rprs normal hours
A461 s'posted Walsall, on R 1m

**10** **County Bridge Service Station, Willenhall**
**G6** (W.65734). Petrol, AA bkdn, serv &
rprs
A454 s'posted Wolverhampton, on L 1¾m

**10** **Grange Garage, Walsall** (W. 26734)
**G7** 07.30-21.00 (09.00-21.00), petrol, bkdn,
serv & rprs normal hours (exc Sun) small
shop
A454 s'posted Walsall, on L ¼m

**11** **Shareshill Service Station, Shareshill**
**G8** National. 07.00-19.00, petrol, derv,
light rprs normal hours
A460 s'posted Wolverhampton ¾m

**12** **Gailey Service Station, Gailey**
**G9** (Standeford 790589) Texaco. 07.00-
23.00, petrol, 24hr bkdn, serv & rprs
08.30-17.30 daily
A5 s'posted Telford, at r'bout ½m

**12** **Dunns Service Station, Penkridge**
**G10** (P. 2260) National. 08.00-18.00, petrol
AA bkdn (night P. 2047)
A5 s'posted Telford, R on A449, on L
2m

## PUBS

**9** **Horse & Jockey, Wednesbury**
**P1** (021-556-0464) Ansells; Victorian pub,
steak bar, lunch 12.00-14.30, dinner
19.00-22.30
A461 s'posted Wednesbury, on R ½m

**9** **Dirty Duck, Walsall** (W. 26408)
**P2** Ansells; town pub, steak bar, meals all
times open (exc Sun)
A461 s'posted Wednesbury, on L 1½m

**11** **Red White & Blue, Featherstone**
**P3** (Wolverhampton 734105) Mitchell &
Butler; family pub, bar meals, lunches
& light evening snacks daily, trad beer,
coaches welcome.
A460 s'posted Wolverhampton, on R
1m

**11** **Elms, Shareshill** (Cheslyn Hay 42063)
**P4** Mitchell & Butler; businessmans lunches a la c, dinners
a la c, Sunday lunch, garden
A460 s'posted Wolverhampton, R to
village, on L ¾m

**11** **Star & Garter, Wedges Mills** (Cheslyn
**P5** Hay 412264) Ansells; large village local,
light lunches daily (cold table Sun),
basket meals in evening, games room,
garden
A460 s'posted Cannock, on L 1m

**12** **Littleton Arms, Penkridge** (P.2287)
**P6** Bass; old coaching house. 9 rooms B&B,
**(RH)** 19.00-21.30, t d'hote and a la c, closed Sun,
bar meals
A5 s'posted Telford, R on A449, on R
2½m

## RESTAURANTS

**10** **Toll House, Willenhall** (W. 65575)
**R1** Bar, lunches & dinners, mainly grills
A454 s'posted Wolverhampton, on L 1½m

## HOTELS

**9** **Crest Motel, Walsall** (W. 33555)
**H1** Bass; *** 106 bedrms with bath & TV,
**(R)** restaurant, bkfst 07.00-09.30, lunch, chefs
table & a la c, dinner 19.00-21.30, Sunday
lunch, bars, light snacks, garden
A461 s'posted Walsall, 1st R, on R 2m

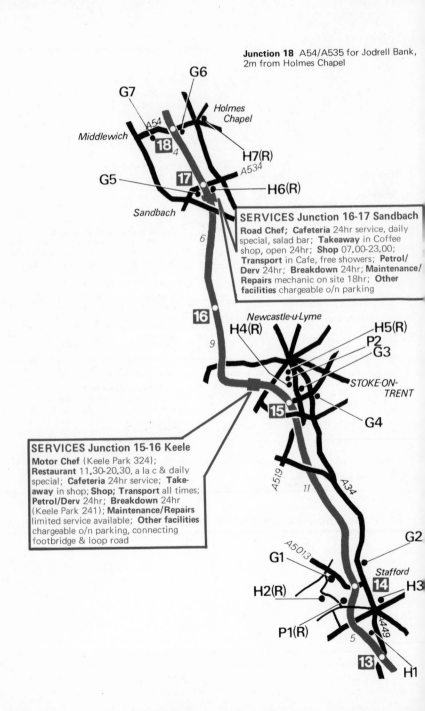

**Junction 18** A54/A535 for Jodrell Bank, 2m from Holmes Chapel

G6

G7

Holmes Chapel

A54

Middlewich

18

4

H7(R)

A534

17

G5

H6(R)

Sandbach

6

**SERVICES Junction 16-17 Sandbach**
**Road Chef; Cafeteria** 24hr service, daily special, salad bar; **Takeaway** in Coffee shop, open 24hr; **Shop** 07.00-23.00; **Transport** in Cafe, free showers; **Petrol/Derv** 24hr; **Breakdown** 24hr; **Maintenance/Repairs** mechanic on site 18hr; **Other facilities** chargeable o/n parking

16

Newcastle-u-Lyme

9

H4(R)

H5(R)

P2

G3

STOKE-ON-TRENT

15

G4

**SERVICES Junction 15-16 Keele**
**Motor Chef** (Keele Park 324); **Restaurant** 11.30-20.30, a la c & daily special; **Cafeteria** 24hr service; **Takeaway** in shop; **Shop; Transport** all times; **Petrol/Derv** 24hr; **Breakdown** 24hr (Keele Park 241); **Maintenance/Repairs** limited service available; **Other facilities** chargeable o/n parking, connecting footbridge & loop road

A519

11

A34

G2

A5013

G1

Stafford

H2(R)

14

H3

P1(R)

A449

5

13

H1

## GARAGES

**14**
**G1**
**Great Bridgford Service Station, Great Bridgford** (Seighford 221) 08.00-19.00 (10.00-18.00 Sun), petrol, bkdn & rprs (08.30-17.30)
A5013 s'posted Stafford, at junction with B5405                    1½m

**14**
**G2**
**Yarlit Bank Garage, Whitgreave** (Sandon 248) Esso. 07.00-19.00, petrol, bkdn serv normal hours, serv & rprs
A34 s'posted Stone, on R            1m

**15**
**G3**
**Swift Service Station, Newcastle-under-Lyme** (N-under-L 627838) petrol, derv, RAC bkdn, serv & rprs. 08.30-21.00 weekdays, 17.00 Sat, on call Sun
A5006 s'posted Newcastle, L on A519, on L            ½m

**15**
**G4**
**Petropolis Filling Station, Stoke-on-Trent** Total. Petrol 24hr prepayment, shop with spares
A5006 s'posted Stoke-on-Trent, on R
¾m

**17**
**G5**
**Hills Garage, Sandbach** (S. 2498) National. 08.30-22.30, petrol, bkdn & rprs
A534 s'posted Sandbach, on L      ¼m

**18**
**G6**
**Cotton Filling Station, Holmes Chapel** Petrol 24hr prepayment
A54 s'posted Holmes Chapel, on R      1m

**18**
**G7**
**Sproston Auto Point, Fernbank** (Middlewich 2071) Burmah. 08.00-20.00, petrol, derv, RAC bkdn, serv & rprs, car hire
A54 s'posted Middlewich, on L      1m

## PUBS

**14**
**P1**
**(R)**
**Holly Bush, Seighford** (S.280) Character pub, restaurant, lunch 12.00-14.30, dinner 20.00-22.30, special dishes & a la c
A501 s'posted Eccleshall, L onto B5405, L through village      2½m

**15**
**P2**
**Copeland Arms, Clayton** (Newcastle-under-Lyme 617677) Ansells; pub in grounds of Clayton Lodge Hotel, cold buffet, hot lunches, evening snacks, patio
A5006 s'posted Newcastle, L on A519 on L      1¼m

## HOTELS

**13**
**H1**
**Garth Hotel, Moss Pit** (Stafford 51402) Banks; 8 bedrm, dining room, businessmans lunch weekdays, Sunday lunch, cold buffet, trad beer
A449 s'posted Stafford, on L      ½m

**14**
**H2**
**(R)**
**Seighford Hall, Seighford** (S. 341) Private; *** Elizabethan mansion, 13 bedrm with bath, restaurant, lunch 12.00-14.00, t d'hote & a la c, dinner 19.00-21.30, a la c
A5013 s'posted Eccleshall, L onto B5405, L into village      2m

**14**
**H3**
**Vine, Stafford** (S. 51071) Banks; *old coaching house, 23 bedrms, lounge, restaurant, lunchtime buffet, evening meals up to 20.30
A5013 s'posted Stafford, on L      2m

**15**
**H4**
**(R)**
**Post House, Newcastle-under-Lyme** (N-u-L 625151) Trust House Forte; *** 106 bedrm, bars with quick meals & snacks, restaurant, bkfst 07.30-10.30 (9.30 Sun), t d'hote & a la c lunches & dinners daily
A5006 s'posted Newcastle, L on A519, on L      ¼m

**15**
**H5**
**(R)**
**Clayton Lodge Hotel, Clayton** (Newcastle-under-Lyme 613093). Ind Coope;*** 52 bedrm, restaurant, daily lunches & dinners, t d'hote & a la c
A5006 s'posted Newcastle, L on A519, on L      1½m

**17**
**H6**
**(R)**
**Saxon Cross Motel, Brereton** (Sandbach 2636) Freehouse ***54 bedrm with bath & TV, restaurant, bkfst 07.30-09.30 (08.00-09.30 Sun), lunch 12.30-14.00, businessmans & a la c, dinners 19.00-21.30 a la c
A534 s'posted Sandbach, on R      ¼m

**18**
**H7**
**(R)**
**Bears Head Hotel, Brereton** (Holmes Chapel 35251) Freehouse; fine Tudor coaching house, 15 bedrms, bathrm, restaurant t d'hote & a la c lunches & dinners(not Sun exc residents), bar meals & snacks, garden, tennis court, bowling green (residents only)
A54 s'posted Holmes Chapel, R onto A50      2m

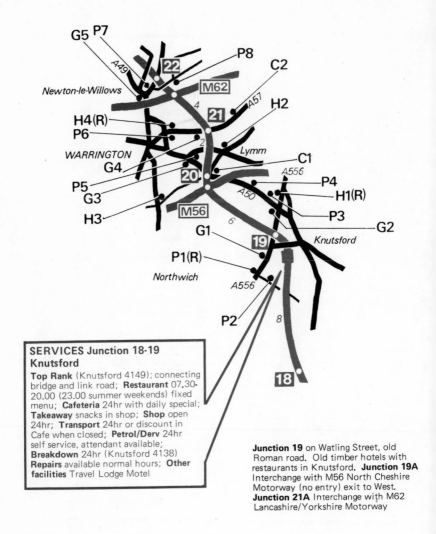

**SERVICES Junction 18-19**
**Knutsford**
**Top Rank** (Knutsford 4149); connecting bridge and link road; **Restaurant** 07.30-20.00 (23.00 summer weekends) fixed menu; **Cafeteria** 24hr with daily special; **Takeaway** snacks in shop; **Shop** open 24hr; **Transport** 24hr or discount in Cafe when closed; **Petrol/Derv** 24hr self service, attendant available; **Breakdown** 24hr (Knutsford 4138) **Repairs** available normal hours; **Other facilities** Travel Lodge Motel

**Junction 19** on Watling Street, old Roman road. Old timber hotels with restaurants in Knutsford. **Junction 19A** Interchange with M56 North Cheshire Motorway (no entry) exit to West. **Junction 21A** Interchange with M62 Lancashire/Yorkshire Motorway

## CAFES

**20**
**C1** **Popular Cafe, High Leigh**
07.00-22.00 (07.00-17.00 Sat, closed Sun), substantial quick snacks
A50 s'posted Knutsford, on L ¼m

**21**
**C2** **Malt Lane Cafe, Hollins Green**
Bkfst & light snacks in small wooden hut, closed Sat midday and all day Sun
A57 s'posted Eccles, on L 1m

## GARAGES

**19**
**G1** **Knutsford Motors, Tabley**
Workshop, rprs, bkdn normal hours
A556 s'posted Chester, on L ½m

**19**
**G2** **Cheshire Way Filling Station, Bucklow Hill**
BP. Petrol 24hr prepayment, shop, spares
A556 s'posted Manchester, on L, at junction with A50 ½m

**20**
**G3** **Grappenhall Service Station, Grappenhall**
08.00-18.00 (10.00-17.00 Sun), serv, rprs, weekdays normal hours, Citroen agent
A50 s'posted Warrington, on R ½m

**21**
**G4** **Woolston Service Station, Warrington**
National. 08.00-22.00 petrol, rprs & serv, normal hours, limited spares
A50 s'posted Warrington, on L 1m

**22**
**G5** **Ace of Clubs, Winwick**
Cleveland. 07.00-21.00, petrol, serv & rprs normal hours, shop, spares, Fiat agent
A49 s'posted Warrington, on L 2m

## PUBS

**19**
**P1**
**(R)** **Smoker Inn, Tabley** (Lower Peover 2338)
Robinsons; celebrated old pub restaurant, lunch 12.30-14.00, dinner 19.30-22.00, (exc Sun), bar meals, gardens
A556 s'posted Chester, on L 1½m

**19**
**P2** **Golden Pheasant, Plumley** (Lower Peover 2261) Lees; old pub, restaurant, bar meals, garden with tables
A556 s'posted Chester, L to village 2m

**19**
**P3** **Kilton Inn, Bucklow Hill** (BH 830420)
Ex-court house, now Inn using old courtroom as restaurant (closed Sun & Mon), bar buffet lunchtime, garden
A556 s'posted Manchester, L on A50 1½m

**20**
**P4** **Bears Paw, High Leigh** (Lymm 2573)
Good bar snacks, trad beer, garden
A50 s'posted Knutsford, on L 1½m

**20**
**P5** **Dog & Dart, Grappenhall** (Warrington 62675) Greenall Whitley; modernised main road pub, trad beer, restaurant (closed Sat lunch & all day Sun) grills, RAC recommended
A50 s'posted Warrington, on R 1½m

**21**
**P6** **Highwayman, Warrington** (W. 32045)
Bass; suburban pub, lunchtime & evening grills; bar snacks
A57 s'posted Warrington, on L 1½m

**22**
**P7** **Swan, Winwick** (Warrington 34202)
Wilsons; mock Tudor, lunches Mon-Fri, sandwiches, trad ale, garden
A49 s'posted Warrington, on A573 on R 1m

**22**
**P8** **General Eliott, Croft** (Culcheth 3264)
Tetleys; lunches & light grills
A579 s'posted Leigh, R to village 1½m

## HOTELS

**19**
**H1**
**(R)** **Swan, Bucklow Hill** (BH. 830295)
Greenall Whitley; old coaching house, ***56 bedrms with bath & TV, restaurant, bkfst 07.30-09.30, lunch 12.30-14.00, t d'hote & a la c, evenings a la c, bar meals always available, garden
A556 s'posted Manchester, on L 2m

**20**
**H2** **Lymm Hotel, Lymm** (L. 2233)
Greenall Whitley; converted private house, **30 bedrm (mostly with bath), restaurant, bar, garden
A50 s'posted Lymm, L into village 2m

**20**
**H3** **Old Vicarage Hotel, Stretton** (Norcott Brook 238) Freehouse; **38 bedrms, restaurant, lunches & dinners, bar meals
A50 s'posted Warrington, L on A5656 to village, on side road 2½m

**21**
**H4**
**(R)** **Paddington House, Warrington**
(Padgate 816742) Freehouse; old private house, ***35 bedrms with bath & TV, restaurant, lunch 12.00-14.00, dinner 19.00-21.30, t d'hote & a la c, bar meals
A57 s'posted Warrington, on R in trees 1½m

# M6. JUNCTIONS 23–31

## SERVICES Junction 27-28 Charnock Richard

**Motor Chef** (Coppull 791497); **Restaurant** 07.30-22.30, blue plate specials, set lunch & a la c, (Coppull 791494); **Cafeteria** 24hr; **Takeaway** 07.30-20.00 (21.30 in summer); **Shop** 07.30-20.00 (21.30 in summer); **Transport** 24hr (alternate sides open at night); **Petrol/Derv** 24hr, attendant available; **Breakdown** 24hr (Coppull 791497); **Maintenance/Repairs** 24 hr, Blue Star. **Other facilities** chargeable o/n parking, \*\*\*Travel Lodge, (Coppull 791746)

**Junction 24** Nbound entry, Sbound exit only. **Junction 30** Interchange with M61 Manchester-Preston Motorway

G5

H4(R)

*A6*

31

PRESTON

*3*

BLACKBURN

30

*A59*

R2

C1(G)

P6

H3(R)

*1*

29

*2*

28

M61

*Leyland*

G4

*A6*

*Chorley*

*8*

*B5250*

*A49*

P5

G3

H2(R)

R1

*B5239*

*B5209*

27

P4(R)

P3

WIGAN

*4*

*A577*

*A49*

*A506*

26

*3*

25A

H1(R)

P2(R)

25

*1*

24

*1*

*Ashton in Makerfield*

23

G2

P1

G1

*A49*

## CAFES

**29** **Clayton Brook Transport Cafe, Clayton**
**C1** **Brook.** 07.00-19.00, limited weekends,
light meals & snacks, service station. Mobil.
**(G)** 09.00-21.00 petrol, derv
A6 s'posted Chorley                              ¾m

## GARAGES

**23** **A & B Motors, Newton-le-Willows**
**G1** (N le W 4411) Fina. Petrol 24hr pre-
payment, serv & rprs, bkdn normal hours,
Leyland agent
A49 s'posted Warrington, in village    1½m

**23** **Haydock Island Service Station,**
**G2** Shell; 07.00-21.00, Fri & Sat open all
night, spares, shop
A580 s'posted St Helens, on exit r'bout
                                                ¼m

**27** **Crow Orchard Filling Station,**
**G3** **Wrightington,** (Standish 423546)
National. 07.00-22.00 (08.00-22.00 Sat
& Sun), petrol, bkdn & rprs normal
hours
B5209 s'posted Parbold, R onto B5250,
on L                                            ¼m

**28** **Leyland Garage, Leyland** (L. 21766)
**G4** Esso. 09.00-18.30, petrol, 24hr bkdn
(Leyland 21765 night), serv & rprs
normal hours
B5256 s'posted Leyland                          ¾m

**31** **Riverside Filling Station, Samlesbury**(S.668)
**G5** Mobil, 08.00-22.00 (21.00 Sun), petrol,
derv, 24hr light bkdn
A59 s'posted Preston, on R                      ¾m

## PUBS

**23** **Pied Bull, Newton le Willows**
**P1** (N le W 4349) Whitley; old roadside pub,
lunches & cold buffet in bar
A49 s'posted Warrington, to village
on L side                                       1m

**23** **Bay Horse, Haydock Park** (Ashton
**P2** 78995) Greenall Whitley; near race-
**(R)** course, small restaurant, lunch Mon-Fri
(Sat if racing) Fri & Sat evenings a la c,
garden
A49 s'posted Wigan to village on R side
                                                1m

**26** **Stag, Wigan** (Wigan 82248)
**P3** Tetleys; pub cum steak house, grills,
buffet bar & snacks
To A577 s'posted Wigan, L onto A577,
on R                                            ½m

**27** **Black Horse, Standish** (S. 421484)
**P4** Greenhall Whitley; modern pub on old
**(R)** site, restaurant for lunches & evening
meals
B5239 s'posted Standish, on R         1m

**27** **Scarsbrick Arms, Wrightington Bar**
**P5** (Eccleston 451048) Burtonwood;
Victorian pub, restaurant, lunches daily,
t d'hote & a la c, bar meals, snacks,
dinner (exc Mon) a la c
B5209 s'posted Parbold, R onto B5250,
through village, on R                           2½m

**29** **Old Hob Inn, Bamber Bridge**
(Preston 36863)
**P6** Burtonwood; small thatched pub, light
lunches, speciality fish dishes, lunchtime
& evenings
A6 s'posted Preston, on L                       ¼m

## RESTAURANTS

**27** **High Moor, Appley Bridge** (AB 2364)
**R1** Picturesque cottage, small restaurant,
lunch 12.00-14.00 (exc Sat) t d'hote &
a la c, dinner a la c, closed Mon
B5209 s'posted Parbold, R to village
                                                2m

**29** **Birch House, Higher Walton** (Preston
**R2** 51366) Converted private house, lunch
12.00-14.30 Mon-Fri, dinner 19.00-
21.30, high teas 16.00-21.30
A6 s'posted Preston, R on A675, on R
                                                1½m

## HOTELS

**26** **Balcony Farm Inn, East Pimbo**
**H1** (Skelmersdale 20401) Early 18C farm,
**(R)** now modern hotel, restaurant, lunch
12.00-14.00, dinner 19.00-21.30 t d'hote
& a la c, bar snacks
A506 s'posted Southport, on L        1m

**27** **Cassinelli's Motor Inn, Standish**
**H2** (S. 421504) Freehouse; ***motel 21
**(R)** bedrms with TV, phone & private bath,
restaurant, bkfst 07.00-9.30, lunch
12.00-14.30, dinner 18.30-22.30, t d'hote
& a la c, cabaret/dinner dance Sat
B5239 s'posted Standish, L onto A49,
on L                                            1m

**29** **Pines, Clayton le Woods** (Preston 38551)
**H3** Freehouse; 21 bedrms**hotel, restaurant,
**(R)** bkfst 07.00-09.30, lunch 12.00-14.00,
dinner 19.00-21.00, t d'hote disco/dinner
Fri, bar meals & snacks, 2 squash courts
A6 s'posted Chorley, on L            1m

**31** **Tickled Trout, Samlesbury** (S. 671)
**H4** ***66 bedrms with TV & bath, restaurant,
**(R)** bkfst 07.00-09.30, lunch 12.00-14.30,
t d'hote & a la c, dinner 19.00-22.30,
a la c, fishing rights on 1 mile of river
A59 s'posted Preston, on R           ½m

# M6. JUNCTIONS 32 – 35 & M55 Blackpool spur

**Junction 32** M55 Blackpool Spur, no Junction 2 at present. **Junction 34** Lancaster A683, 3m. Belfast car ferry from Heysham, A683 Lancaster, A589 Heysham, 5m

**SERVICES Junction 32-33 Forton**
**Top Rank** (Forton 791775); **Restaurant** 12.00-21.45 (12.00-20.00 weekends), mainly grills, a la c & t d'hote; **Cafeteria** 24hr, daily specials; **Takeaway** 07.00-23.00; **Shop** 07.00-23.00 (24hr some summer weekends); **Transport** no special facilities; **Petrol/Derv** 24hr, attendant available; **Breakdown** 24hr service (Forton 791666). **Maintenance/Repairs** light rprs; **Other facilities** chargeable o/n parking, spectacular view from Tower top

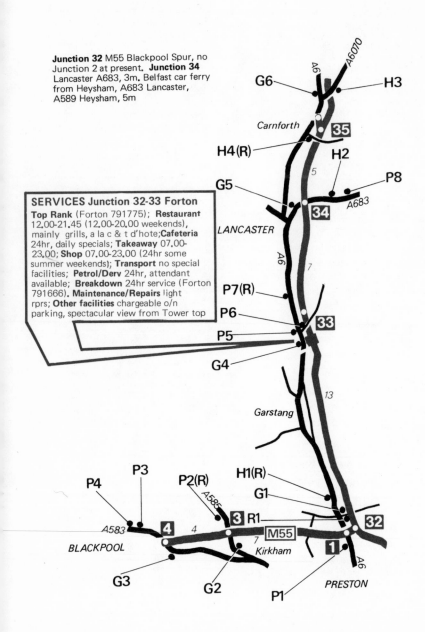

## GARAGES

**155 / 1 / G1** **Kinders Service Station, Broughton**
(Preston 863922) BP. 07.00-22.00
(09.00-22.00 Sun), petrol, derv, AA **
rprs, AA bkdn (P. 3032 night)
A6 s'posted Garstang, on R ½m

**55 / 3 / G2** **Station Road Service Station**
(Kirkham 682404) Shell. Petrol 24hr
prepayment, AA/RAC bkdn serv & rprs
A585 s'posted Kirkham, on L 1¼m

**55 / 4 / G3** **Clock Garage, Kirkham, Blackpool**
(B. 62150) Petrol 24hr prepayment,
serv 07.30-22.00 daily, light bkdn
A583 s'posted Kirkham, on L ½m

**33 / G4** **New Holly Service Station, Forton**
(F. 791424) Shell. 07.30-19.00, petrol,
derv, 24hr light bkdn, serv & rprs
A6 s'posted Garstang, L to Forton, on R 2½m

**34 / G5** **Caton Road Garage, Lancaster** (L. 2917)
National. 07.00-20.30 daily, petrol,
AA bkdn & recovery (L. 65767) night;
serv & rprs normal hours, limited spares
A683 s'posted Lancaster ½m

**35 / G6** **Wayside Garage, Carnforth** (C. 2460)
Texaco. 08.00-20.00, petrol, AA bkdn,
AA rprs & serv normal hours
A6 s'posted Kendal, L fork, on R 2m

## PUBS

**55 / 1 / P1** **Black Bull, Preston**
Bass; suburban roadside pub, lunches
Mon-Fri, snacks other times
A6 s'posted Preston, on R ¾m

**55 / 3 / (R)** **Blue Anchor, Greenhalgh** (Weedon 283)
Thwaites; farmhouse pub, bar lunches
(exc Sat), trad beer, restaurant, garden
A585 s'posted Fleetwood, on R ½m

**55 / 4 / P3** **Clifton Arms, Blackpool**
Greenall Whitley; red brick pub,
lunches Mon-Fri, snacks weekends and
evenings
A583 s'posted Blackpool, on L ½m

**55 / 4 / P4** **Clarence, Blackpool**
Thwaites; family pub, lunches Mon-Fri,
evening meals
A583 s'posted Blackpool, on L 1m

**33 / P5** **Bay Horse, Bay Horse Ellel** (Forton 791204)
Mitchell; 17C country pub, 2 rooms B&B,
bar meals, trad local beer
A6 s'posted Garstang, L on old road, on R ½m

**33 / P6** **Foxholes, Bay Horse Ellel** (Forton 791237)
Freehouse; old country house, *10 room
pub, B&B, lunches & dinners a la c,
garden
A6 s'posted Garstang, L on old road, R
under railway ¾m

**33 / P7 / (R)** **Stork, Galgate** (Galgate 234)
Freehouse; old fishermans haunt,
restaurant, lunch 12.00-14.30, dinner
18.00 (19.00 Sun)-22.00, grills & a la c,
light bar snacks
A6 s'posted Lancaster, then L to village 2½m

**34 / P8** **Ship Inn, Caton** (C. 770265)
Coaching house, 4 rooms B&B, bar
lunches, evening meals
A683 s'posted Kirby Lonsdale, on R 2¾m

## RESTAURANTS

**M55 / 1 / R1** **Orchard Restaurant, Broughton**
(B. 862208) Lunch (exc Mon),
dinner (exc Sun & Mon), t d'hote &
a la c, trad English cooking, dinner
dance Thurs & Sat
A6 s'posted Garstang, R onto B5269,
R before M bridge 1m

## HOTELS

**M55 / 1 / H1 / (R)** **Barton Grange, Barton** (Broughton
862551) Enlarged house in own grounds
**32 room (most with own bath),
restaurant, lunch 12.30-14.00, dinner
18.30-21.30, t d'hote & a la c, lounge,
gardens
A6 s'posted Garstang, on R 2m

**34 / H2** **Scarthwaite Hotel, Crook o'lune**
(Caton 770267) Freehouse; old Victorian
house in own grounds, 6 room, B&B, bar,
basket meals lunchtime, dancing Fri &
Sat
A683 s'posted Kirby Lonsdale, on R 1½m

**35 / H3** **Longlands Hotel, Tewitfield** (Burton
781256) Freehouse; country pub near
canal, 6 rooms B&B, TV lounge, bar meals,
fishing locally, patio
A6 s'posted Kendal, then R onto A6070 1½m

**35 / H4 / (R)** **Royal Station, Carnforth** (C. 2033)
Victorian, **hotel, 9 room, B&B,
restaurant, bkfst 08.00-09.30, lunch
12.00-14.00, dinner 19.00-21.00,
t d'hote & a la c, bar meals
A6 s'posted Carnforth, on R 2m

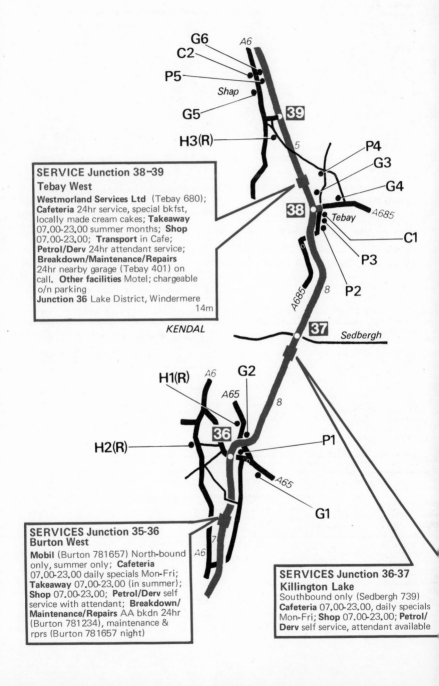

G6
C2
P5
*Shap*
G5
**39**
H3(R)
*A6*
*5*

P4
G3
G4

SERVICE Junction 38-39
Tebay West
**Westmorland Services Ltd** (Tebay 680);
**Cafeteria** 24hr service, special bkfst,
locally made cream cakes; **Takeaway**
07.00-23.00 summer months; **Shop**
07.00-23.00; **Transport** in Cafe;
**Petrol/Derv** 24hr attendant service;
**Breakdown/Maintenance/Repairs**
24hr nearby garage (Tebay 401) on
call. **Other facilities** Motel; chargeable
o/n parking
**Junction 36** Lake District, Windermere
14m

**38**
*Tebay*    *A685*
C1
P3
P2

*A685*

*8*

**37**    *Sedbergh*

*KENDAL*

H1(R)    G2
*A6*
*A65*
H2(R)
**36**
P1
G1
*A65*

*8*

SERVICES Junction 35-36
Burton West
**Mobil** (Burton 781657) North-bound
only, summer only; **Cafeteria**
07.00-23.00 daily specials Mon-Fri;
**Takeaway** 07.00-23.00 (in summer);
**Shop** 07.00-23.00; **Petrol/Derv** self
service with attendant; **Breakdown/
Maintenance/Repairs** AA bkdn 24hr
(Burton 781234), maintenance &
rprs (Burton 781657 night)

*7*
*A6*

SERVICES Junction 36-37
Killington Lake
Southbound only (Sedbergh 739)
**Cafeteria** 07.00-23.00, daily specials
Mon-Fri; **Shop** 07.00-23.00; **Petrol/
Derv** self service, attendant available

## CAFES

**38**
**C1** Riverside Cafe, Tebay
08.30-17.00 Mon-Fri, 08.30-12.00 Sat,
light snacks
A685 s'posted Kendal, on R          1¾m

**39**
**C2** Southview Cafe, Shap
08.00-17.30 daily, bkfst, lunches, teas,
snacks
A6 s'posted Shap, on L          ½m

## GARAGES

**36**
**G1** Canal Garage, Crooklands  (C.401)
Shell Petrol, derv, 24hr propane gas,
AA/RAC bkdn service — on call 24hr
A65 s'posted Kendal, on R          ½m

**36**
**G2** Crooklands Garage, Crooklands (C. 414)
08.00-19.00, petrol, rprs & serv normal
hours
A65 s'posted Kendal, on L          ½m

**38**
**G3** Tebay Services, Tebay  (Orton 688)
Shell 24hr petrol, derv, propane, AA/RAC
bkdn & call out service, serv & rprs normal
hours, hot drinks &  pies available
B6260 s'posted Appleby, on L          ¼m

**38**
**G4** Lune Valley Service Station, Tebay
ICI. 24hr petrol, diesel, closed 21.00 Sat-
09.00 Sun, limited spares, shop
A685 s'posted Brough, on R          ½m

**39**
**G5** Simpson Garage, Shap  (S.212)
Shell 08.00-19.00 Mon-Sat, petrol,
derv, AA bkdn (S. 236 night) AA garage
normal hours, Leyland agent, spares
A6 s'posted Shap, on L          ½m

**39**
**G6** Fell Garage, Shap  (S.219) Texaco
08.00-18.00 petrol, derv, 24hr bkdn
service, rprs & service normal hours,
emergency call out
A6 s'posted Shap, through village on R
          1m

## PUBS

**36**
**P1** Plough, Lupton  (Crookland 227)
Vaux; country pub, 7 rooms B&B, bar
meals lunchtime & evenings, trad beer.
children's games room, fishing locally,
garden
A65 s'posted Kirby Lonsdale, on R          1½m

**38**
**P2** Barnaby Rudge, Tebay  (Orton 328)
Freehouse; galleried restaurant serving
lunches & dinners, bar meals, trad beer,
outside seating
A685 s'posted Kendal, on R          ½m

**38**
**P3** Junction, Tebay  (Orton 232)
Freehouse; Victorian railway pub, 12
rooms B&B, all meals inc. bkfst, (music
weekends) caravan site, fishing
available
A685 s'posted Kendal, on R          ½m

**38**
**P4** George, Orton  (O. 229)
Youngers; 7 bedrms, bar meals, trad
beer, garden, fishing available
B6260 s'posted Appleby, on L in
village          2m

**39**
**P5** Greyhound, Shap  (S. 208)
Whitbread; old coaching house, 10
rooms, B&B, bar meals
A6 s'posted Shap, on R in village          1m

## HOTELS

**36**
**H1**
**(R)** Crooklands Hotel, Crooklands  (C.432)
Freehouse; old farmhouse, ***20 bedrms
most with bath, B&B, restaurant, bkfst
07.30-09.30, lunch 12.00-14.00 t d'hote
& a la c, dinner 19.30-21.30 a la c, dinner
dances Sat during winter, bar meals, local
trad beer
A65 s'posted Kendal, on R          1m

**36**
**H2**
**(R)** Blue Bell, Heversham  (Milnthorpe 3159)
Freehouse; ex vicarage, ***20 bedrms
(most with bath), restaurant, lunch 12.30-
13.30, dinner 19.00-20.30 a la c, bar
meals, garden
A65 s'posted Kendal, L onto B6385, R
to Heversham, at junction with A6          3m

**39**
**H3**
**(R)** Shap Wells Hotel, Nr Shap  (S. 628)
Freehouse; old farmhouse, ***70 bedrm
hotel in own grounds, restaurant, bkfst
08.00-09.30, lunch 12.00-14.00, dinner
19.00-21.00, t d'hote & a la c, bar meals,
tennis court, fishing available
A6 s'posted Kendal, L to hotel road  2½m

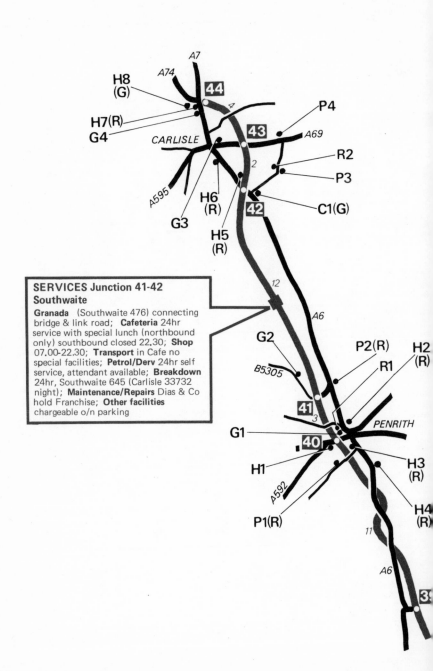

H8
(G)

H7(R)
G4

CARLISLE

A7
A74
44
4

P4

43
A69

R2

P3

A595

H6
(R)

G3

2

42

H5
(R)

C1(G)

12

A6

**SERVICES Junction 41-42**
**Southwaite**
**Granada** (Southwaite 476) connecting
bridge & link road; **Cafeteria** 24hr
service with special lunch (northbound
only) southbound closed 22.30; **Shop**
07.00-22.30; **Transport** in Cafe no
special facilities; **Petrol/Derv** 24hr self
service, attendant available; **Breakdown**
24hr, Southwaite 645 (Carlisle 33732
night); **Maintenance/Repairs** Dias & Co
hold Franchise; **Other facilities**
chargeable o/n parking

G2

B5305

41

3

G1

40

H1

A592

P1(R)

P2(R)

R1

H2
(R)

PENRITH

H3
(R)

H4
(R)

11

A6

3

## CAFES

**42**
**C1**
**(G)**
**Golden Fleece Service Station Cafe,**
**Carleton;**  Hot drinks, snacks; Garage;
National. (Carlisle 26565) petrol, derv
24hr Mon-Fri, 08.00-21.00 Sat & Sun,
24hr bkdn & rprs same hours o/night
stop, shop
A6 s'posted Penrith, at r'bout          ¼m

## GARAGE

**40**
**G1**
**Ullswater Road Garage, Penrith** (P.4545)
Esso. 08.00-18.00 (closed Sun), petrol
08.00-20.00, AA **bkdn & rprs (P.2321
night), VW & Audi agent
A66 s'posted Appleby, L onto A592, on L
¼m

**41**
**G2**
**Woodlands Garage, Catterlen** (Penrith 4019)
Esso. 08.00-19.00, petrol, derv 08.00-
19.00 light bkdn recovery, serv & light
rprs, small shop
B5305 s'posted Wigton, on R          2m

**43**
**G3**
**McKenzie Motors, Carlisle** (C. 25177)
ICI. 08.00-22.30, petrol, AA bkdn
(34121 night Carlisle) serv & rprs normal
hours, Chrysler agent
A69 s'posted Carlisle, on R          1¼m

**44**
**G4**
**Kingstown Filling Station, Kingstown**
Shell. 24hr prepayment machine,
attendant, 08.00-19.00 every day
A7 s'posted Carlisle, on R          ¼m

## PUBS

**40**
**P1**
**(R)**
**Queens Head, Penrith** (P. 3219)
Tetley's, old pub, bar meals, restaurant,
lunch 12.00-14.00, dinner 18.30-21.30.
personal home cooking
A66 s'posted Appleby, R onto A6, R
onto B5320, on R          2m

**41**
**P2**
**(R)**
**Stonybeck, Owscar** (Penrith 2369)
Freehouse; old farmhouse, restaurant,
bar meals, evening grills, garden
A6 s'posted Carlisle, at r'bout          ½m

**42**
**P3**
**Crown, Wetheral** (W. 60208)
Georgian building with courtyard, meals
lunchtime & evenings
B6263 s'posted Wetheral, in village   2½m

**43**
**P4**
**Queens Arms, Warwick**
Tetleys; small pub by-passed by new
road, light meals
A69 s'posted Hexham, R on loop road
into village          1¼m

## RESTAURANTS

**40**
**R1**
**Glen Cottage Hotel, Penrith** (P. 2221)
*7 room small town house, bkfst
08.00-09.00, lunches & dinners a la c &
t d'hote
A66 s'posted Appleby, L onto A592 to
town centre          1½m

**42**
**R2**
**Fantails Restaurant, Wetheral** (W. 60239)
Converted cottage 10.00-21.00, a la c
B6263 s'posted Wetheral, in village   2½m

## HOTELS

**40**
**H1**
**Limes, Redhills, Stainton** (Penrith 3343)
House in own grounds, B&B (dinner
available) lounge
A66 s'posted Keswick, L into hamlet
(old road), on L          ½m

**40**
**H2**
**(R)**
**George, Penrith** (P. 4019)
Old coaching house in town centre,
**34 bedrms, B&B, TV lounge, restaurant
A66 s'posted Appleby, L onto A592 to
town centre          1¼m

**40**
**H3**
**(R)**
**Crown, Penrith** (P. 2566)
Whitbread; 16 bedrms, restaurant, lunch
12.00-14.00, dinner 19.00-20.30, a la c
A66 s'posted Appleby, R onto A6          2m

**40**
**H4**
**(R)**
**Clifton Hill Hotel, Penrith** (P. 2717)
Converted private house in own grounds,
**22 bedrm with bath, restaurant, bar
meals, garden
A66 s'posted Appleby, R onto A6, on R
2m

**42**
**H5**
**(R)**
**Carrow House, Carleton** (Carlisle 32073)
Victorian hotel, 14 bedrms, restaurant
07.15-22.00 (all day service for a la c
meals)
A6 s'posted Carlisle, on R in cul de sac
½m

**42**
**H6**
**(R)**
**Hilltop Motel, Carlisle** (C. 29255)
Purpose built ***123 bedrms with bath,
B&B, restaurant, bkfst 07.30-09.00,
lunch 12.00-14.00, dinner 19.00-22.00
t d'hote & a la c, bar snacks, garden
A6 s'posted Carlisle, on L          2½m

**44**
**H7**
**(R)**
**Crest Motel, Kingstown** (Carlisle 31201)
Bass; modern 98 bedrms with TV &
phone, bar, lounge, restaurant, bkfst
07.30-09.30, lunch 12.30-14.00, t d'hote
& a la c buffet open 09.00-17.00 week-
days only, bar meals, garden
A7 s'posted Carlisle, on R          ¼m

**44**
**H8**
**(G)**
**Truck Inn Motel, Kingstown** (Carlisle
34192) 38 bedrms, mainly for transport
drivers, TV lounge, cafeteria; garage
24hr petrol, derv, security park
A7 s'posted Carlisle, R by Crest
Motel on L          ¼m

# M8. Edinburgh-Glasgow-Renfrew

**Junction 2** Start of M, a continuation of A8 dual carriageway out of Edinburgh. **Junction 6** Temporary end of M8; continue to Glasgow via A8 to M73 Junction 1 joining Glasgow city M system. Confused junction numbering system in Glasgow. **Junction 7** M8 restarts W of Glasgow. **Junction 9** Glasgow Airport (Renfrew). **Junction 11** Erskine Bridge — tolls 15p cars, 50p lorries. **Junction 12** End of M, to Greenock and Gourock

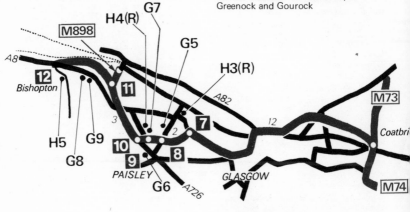

## GARAGES

**2** **Western Auto Co, Newbridge**
**G1** BP. 24hr prepayment self serv machine, derv available
A89 s'posted Uphall, on L ¼m

**3** **Livingston Service Station, Livingston**
**G2** (L. 32660) 07.30-22.00, self serv shop, bkdn & rprs normal hours
A899 s'posted Livingston, on L 1½

**4** **Bathgate Service, Bathgate**
**G3** 24hr prepayment, self serv petrol
B7002 s'posted Bathgate, R onto B7006 s'posted Broxburn, on L 1½

**6** **Swift Service Station, Chapelhall**
**G4** (Holytown 733388) 24hr bkdn serv (night Airdrie 63096)
A73 s'posted Airdrie, on L 1m

**8** **Arklestone Service Station, Renfrew**
**G5** Shell. 07.00-22.00 (08.00-21.00 Sat & Sun) petrol, derv, small shop
A741 s'posted Renfrew, on R ¼m

**8** **McGlynns, Scotts Road, Paisley**
**G6** (Glasgow 8899130) AA bkdn (night 8843990), spares, rprs & maintenance normal hours
A741 s'posted Paisley, on R 1m

**9** **Gaelic Filling Station, Airport** (Glasgow 8878309) Gulf. 24hr attendant serv,
**G7** 24hr bkdn, serv & rprs normal hours
To Airport, R on perimeter road ½m

**12** **Bishopton Garage, Bishopton**
**G8** Texaco. 08.00-18.00 petrol, derv, limited services
A8 s'posted Renfrew, on L 1m

**12** **Holmparts Motors, Bishopton** (B.2511)
**G9** AA bkdn serv
A8 s'posted Renfrew, on R 1m

## CAFES

**5** **Burnside Transport Cafe, West Benhar**
**C1** 06.30-20.00 Mon-Fri, 07.00-23.00 Sat, closed Sun
A7057 s'posted Shotts, L onto A7066 s'posted Harthill, on L 1m

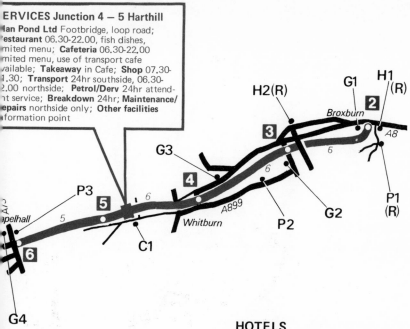

## PUBS

**Bridge Inn, Ratho** (Edinburgh 3331320)
Drybroughs; canalside character pub, barge
as floating restaurant in evenings, also
Glasgow underground coach as shore
restaurant, lunch 12.00-14.00, dinner
19.00-22.00, Mon-Sat, t d'hote & a la c,
book well in advance for an evening
afloat 19.00-23.00 (barge cruises along
the canal) bar lunches, garden
A8 s'posted Edinburgh, R to village, on R
1½m

**Livingston, Livingston Village** (L.31081)
Drybroughs; enlarged village pub, swamped
by new development, 7 rooms B&B,
restaurant, bar lunches, garden
A899 s'posted Livingston, R to Livingston
village, L into village                          2½m

**Glyn Hotel, Chapelhall** (Airdrie 68159)
Small village pub, 5 rooms B&B, bar
lunches & dinner
A73 s'posted Airdrie, on R          2m

**Griffin Hotel, Newhouse** (Cleland 860277)
Freehouse, isolated main road pub, 4
rooms B&B, lunches & dinners t d'hote,
high teas, garden
A8 s'posted Coatbridge, L onto 799 to
Holytown, on R                          ½m

## HOTELS

**Norton Hotel, Ingleston** (Edinburgh
3331275) Freehouse; character small
hotel in own grounds, 10 bedrms (bath
& TV) lunches, dinners, garden
A8 s'posted Edinburgh, R opp Airport
1m

**Houston House Hotel, Uphall** (Broxburn
3831) 16C lairds fortified home in own
grounds,***hotel, 29 bedrms (bath & TV)
restaurant,bkfst 08.15-09.30,lunch 12.00-
14.00, dinner 19.30-21.30, both t d'hote,
advisable to book well in advance, bar
snacks, golf
A899 s'posted Livingston to r'bout, back
under M8 to Uphall, on L          2m

**Glenhill Hotel, Renfrew** (Glasgow
8865555) Freehouse; modernised
Victorian **hotel in own grounds, 47
bedrms (bath & TV), restaurant, bkfst
07.00-10.00, lunch 12.00-14.30, dinner
18.00-22.00, both a la c & t d'hote, bars,
dinner dance Fri & Sat evenings, folk
music Wed & Sun
A741 s'posted Renfrew, on R          ¼m

**Excelsior Hotel, Airport** (Glasgow
8871212) Trust House Forte; modern
hotel, 305 bedrms (bath & TV), restaurant,
bkfst 06.30-09.00, lunch 12.30-14.30,
t d'hote & a la c, dinner 18.30-22.30, a la c
& carvery, disco Sun evening (exc high
summer)
To Airport, on R          ¼m

**Gleddock House, Langbank** (L. 711)
Private house in own grounds, 16 bedrms
(some with bath), B&B available, garden
B789 s'posted Crosslee, on R          1½m

# M9. Edinburgh-Stirling

## JUNCTIONS 1–7, M8000 & M876

**Junction 1** Access from SE only, **M8000** spur to **Forth Bridge,** tolls 25p cars, 50p lorries, 15p cycles. Motorway between Junctions 8-9 not yet complete, use M876 to A9

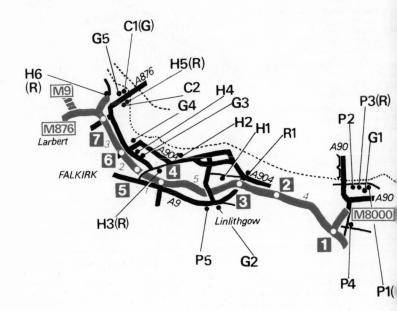

## CAFES

**7 / C1 / G)**
**Silver Link, Kincardine Bridge** (Airth 256)
Transport Cafe, 07.00-20.00 (exc Sat &
Sun), all meals & snacks, transport
accommodation Mon-Fri, filling station,
petrol, derv
A876 s'posted Kincardine, on L          2m

**7 / C2**
**Pine and Oak, Kincardine Bridge** (Airth
393) Self serv cafe & restaurant, all meals,
grills, snacks, small shop
A876 s'posted Kincardine, on R          2m

## GARAGES

**1 / G1**
**Hawes Garage, South Queensferry**
(Edinburgh 3311796) Petrol normal hours,
AA bkdn serv
M8000 spur, A8000 into village, R to
Forth rail bridge, on R          2m

**3 / G2**
**Greenpark Garage, Linlithgow** (L.2118)
Petrol normal hours, AA bkdn (night
L. 4489), serv & rprs, Ford agent
A803 s'posted Linlithgow, on L          1¾m

**6 / G3**
**Earls Gate Service Station, Earlsgate**
Esso. 07.00-19.00 (10.00-17.00 Sun),
petrol, derv
A904 s'posted Grangemouth, R on
A905, on L          ½m

**6 / G4**
**Grange Service Station, Grangemouth**
Esso. 07.30-20.00 (10.00-16.00 Sun),
petrol, derv, light serv & rprs normal
hours
A904 s'posted Grangemouth, on R          1¾m

**7 / G5**
**Kincardine Bridge Filling Station**
Shell. 08.00-20.00, petrol, derv, serv &
rprs normal hours
A876 s'posted Kincardine, on L          2½m

## PUBS

**1 / P1 / (R)**
**Hawes Inn, South Queensferry**
(Edinburgh 3311990) Vaux; 19C inn
at foot of Forth rail bridge, 9 rooms B&B,
TV lounge, restaurant, lunch 12.00-14.00
a la c & t d'hote, dinner 19.00-21.30
a la c, bar lunches weekdays
M8000 spur, A8000 into village, R to
Forth rail bridge, on R          2m

**1 / P2**
**Queensferry Hotel, South Queensferry**
(Edinburgh 3311298) Vaux; backing
onto Firth of Forth, 6 rooms B&B,
evening meal available, lunches (exc Sun),
bar snacks
M8000 spur, A8000 into village, R to
Forth rail bridge, on L          1¾m

**1 / P3 / (R)**
**Sealscraig Hotel, South Queensferry**
(Edinburgh 3311098) Freehouse;
overlooking Firth of Forth, 8 rooms B&B,
TV lounge, restaurant, bkfst 07.45-09.30,
lunch 12.00-14.30, t d'hote & a la c,
dinner 18.30-21.30 a la c
M8000 spur, A8000 into village, R to
Forth rail bridge, on L          1¾m

**1 / P4**
**New Liston Arms, Kirkliston**
(Edinburgh 3333214) Freehouse; stately
small town pub, 7 rooms B&B, bar lunches
Mon-Fri, music & groups Thurs, Fri, Sat
& Sun
M8000 spur, R onto A8000 s'posted
Kirkliston, on R          1m

**3 / P5**
**West Port, Linlithgow** (L. 2126)
Freehouse; 16C character pub, 6 rooms
B&B, lunches (locally renowned) Mon-Fri,
limited snacks at all times
A803 s'posted Linlithgow, R in town,
on R          1½m

## RESTAURANTS

**3 / R1**
**Champany, Champany, Linlithgow**
(Philpstown 532) Lunch 12.00-14.30
t d'hote & a la c, dinner 19.00-21.30
a la c (closed Sun)
A904 s'posted Bo'ness, on R          ½m

## HOTELS

**3 / H1**
**Allanvale Hotel, Linlithgow** (L. 3229)
Freehouse; isolated farm in own grounds,
7 rooms B&B, bar lunches, restaurant,
garden, booking advisable
A803 s'posted Linlithgow, R on minor
road, L at junction, on L          1m

**5 / H2**
**Leapark, Grangemouth** (G. 2331)
**hotel, 31 bedrms, restaurant
B9143 s'posted Grangemouth, R onto
A904, on L          2m

**5 / H3 / (R)**
**Inchyra Grange, Polmont** (P. 711911)
Freehouse; 16C country house in own
grounds, ***hotel, 33 bedrms (with
colour TV), lounge, restaurant, bkfst
07.00-10.00 (exc Sun), lunch 12.30-
14.00, dinner 19.00-21.30, t d'hote &
a la c, dinner dance Sat & Sun, high teas
17.00-18.30 Sat & Sun, bar snacks,
garden
B9143, R to village, R at junc, on R  1m

**6 / H4**
**Hotel International, Grangemouth**
(G. 72456) Freehouse; converted house,
4 bedrms, TV lounge, bar lunches and
evening meals, country & western music
Thurs, garden
A904 s'posted Grangemouth, R on
A905, on R          ½m

**7 / H5 / (R)**
**Airth Castle Hotel, Airth** (A. 411)
Freehouse; castle built in 1408, now
modernised, 19 bedrms with TV,
restaurant, lunch 12.00-14.30 a la c,
dinner 19.00-21.45 (21.00 Sun), French
cuisine, bar, fishing, tennis, badminton,
garden
B9036 s'posted Airth to village, on L  1m

**7 / H6 / (R)**
**Pow Foulis Manor Hotel, Bothkenner**
(Airth 268) Freehouse; old manor house
in own grounds, chalet, 16 bedrms with
TV, lounges, restaurant, bkfst 07.00-09.00
lunch 12.00-14.30 (exc Sat), dinner 19.00-
21.30, t d'hote & a la c, high teas Sun,
garden
A876 s'posted Kincardine, R on minor
road, to private road          2m

# M9. JUNCTIONS 9-11 & M80

**M80** starts as continuation of A80 from Glasgow, linking with M9 at Auchenbowie. **M876** links M80 with M9 at Junction 7 and with Kincardine Bridge. **Junction 11** Present end of M, planned to link with Perth and M90

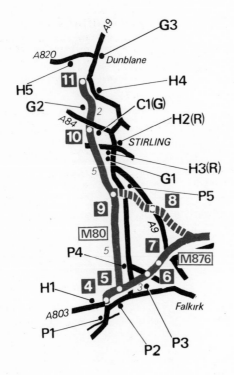

## CAFES

**10**
**C1**
**(G)**
**Riverway Self Service Restaurant, Kildeane** (Stirling 5734) 09.00-16.00 daily in summer, restaurant 11.00-19.00 all meals & teas, Sat dinner dance; garage, Burmah, 08.00-22.00, cut price petrol
A84 s'posted Stirling, R onto minor road, by river                                ½m

## GARAGES

**9**
**G1**
**Morrison Garage, Whim of Milton** (Bannockburn 811411) 07.30-20.30 (09.00 Sun), petrol, bkdn, rprs, Datsun agent
A80 s'posted Stirling, on L                      ¾m

**10**
**G2**
**Fordside Garage, Kildeane** (Stirling 4791) Petrol, serv & rprs normal hours, bkdn
A84 s'posted Callander, on R              ¾m

**11**
**G3**
**Davidson, Dunblane** (D.823557) Shell. 07.30-20.00, petrol, derv, 24hr bkdn (night D. 823274), AA serv & rprs normal hours
A9 s'posted Perth, on R                        1m

## PUBS

**80**
**4**
**P1**
**Castle Cary Hotel, Castle Cary** (Banknock 233) Tennants; popular village pub, 4 rooms B&B, bar lunches, garden
A80 s'posted Cumbernauld, R to Castle Cary, on R                                      ¾m

**80**
**4**
**P2**
**Masonic Inn, Longcroft** Bass; basic village bar, lunches daily in lounge (exc Sun)
A803 s'posted Falkirk, on R              1m

**80**
**4**
**P3**
**Royal Hotel, Bonnybridge** (B. 2454) Tennants; stately building, B&B
A803 s'posted Falkirk, on L              1m

**80**
**4**
**P4**
**Crown, Dennyloanhead** (Bonnybridge 2453) Tennants; small village pub, 3 rooms B&B
A803 s'posted Falkirk, L on A872, to village, on L                                        1m

**9**
**P5**
**Bannockburn Hotel, Bannockburn** (B. 813456) Freehouse; small town hotel, 3 rooms B&B, bar snacks
A9 s'posted Bannockburn, L to village, on L                                            1½m

## HOTELS

**80**
**4**
**H1**
**Gordon Arms Hotel, Banknock** Freehouse; old country house in own grounds
A803 s'posted Kilsyth, on R              1m

**9**
**H2**
**(R)**
**Sword Hotel, Stirling** (S. 3338) Scottish & Newcastle; modern 5 bedrm hotel, lounge, restaurant, bkfst 07.30-0.930, lunch, dinner 19.00-20.45 a la c, bar meals
A80 s'posted Stirling, R onto A905, on L
                                                      2½m

**9**
**H3**
**(R)**
**King Robert Hotel, Whim of Milton** (Bannockburn 811666) Scottish & Newcastle; modern hotel near 1314 battleground, 21 bedrms (with TV & bath), restaurant, bkfst 07.30-09.30, lunches, dinners 19.00-20.45, a la c, bar meals
A80 s'posted Stirling, on L            1¾m

**11**
**H4**
**Queens Hotel, Bridge of Allan** (BoA 833268) Freehouse; Victorian hotel, 14 bedrms (TV & showers), lounge, bkfst, lunch & dinner for non-residents, bar meals, fishing available
A9 s'posted Bridge of Allan, on R    1½m

**11**
**H5**
**Westland Hotel, Dunblane** (D. 822118) Freehouse; small house in own grounds, 8 rooms B&B or full board, restaurant, bar meals, dinner dances Sat, garden
A9 s'posted Perth, L onto A820 s'posted Doune, on R                                      2¼m

# M20. Mid Kent

Not yet completed, presumed junction numbers are given. Open Swanley-Hollingbourne except gap between Junctions 2-3 (work in progress), with planned extensions to Ashford and Folkestone. M25 Swanley-Dartford Tunnel is part of South London orbital road (tunnel toll 25p for cars). M26 will link M25 with M20 at Wrotham to serve London Airport

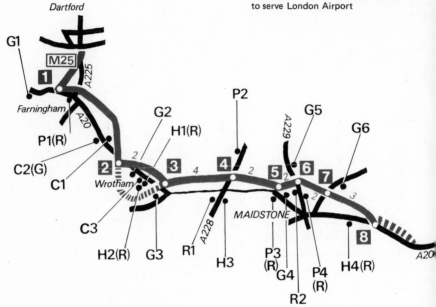

**Junction 1/2** Brands Hatch 2m.
**Junctions 2/3** Use A20. **Junction 6**
A229 link with M2, 3m **Junction 7**
A249 for Sittingbourne and Sheerness ferry to Holland

## CAFES

**2 C1** **Millview Cafe/Tea Gardens, West Kingsdown** Opposite old working wind-mill, 09.00-16.00 (10.00-18.00 Sat & Sun) light meals, snacks, mainly home cooking
A20 s'posted London, on R ¼m

**2 C2 (G)** **Clearways, West Kingsdown** (WK. 2496) B&B for 14 transport drivers, 06.00-19.00 (10.00-18.00 Sun). Light meals, special of the day. Garage, 07.30-18.00 (09.00-18.00 Sun) petrol only
A20 s'posted London, on L 1m

**3 C3** **Oakdene Transport Cafe, Wrotham Hill** 06.30-18.00 Mon-Fri, meals, snacks
A20 s'posted London, on R 1m

## GARAGES

**1 G1** **Dawes Garage, Swanley** (Swanley 62211) Petrol/derv normal hours, AA bkdn recov serv
A20 s'posted London, R into village 2½m

**2 G2** **West Kingsdown Filling Station** Texaco. 24hr self serv, petrol (no night shift help) attendant available by day. Shop, accessories
A20 s'posted Maidstone, on L ¼m

**3 G3** **Wrotham Heath Service, Wrotham Heath** (Borough Green 883255) Shell. 06.00-20.30 (closed Sun) petrol, light bkdn when open for petrol, serv & rprs normal hours
A20 s'posted Maidstone, R onto A25, on R ¼m

**5 G4** **Tudor Garage, Maidstone** Mobil. 07.30-20.00 (09.00-18.00 Sun), petrol only, serv & rprs normal hours, spares and accessories
A20 s'posted Maidstone, on R ¾m

**6 G5** **Cossington Filling Station, Cossington** Shell. 07.00-21.00 (09.00-18.00 Sun) self service, petrol/derv
A229 s'posted Chatham, on R 1m

**7 G6** **Highland Garage, Detling** (Maidstone 39864) 07.00-20.00 (08.00-20.00 Sun) petrol, diesel, 24hr bkdn, rprs, spares & accessories
A249 s'posted Sittingbourne, on R 2½m

## PUBS

**1 P1 (R)** **Lion, Farningham** (Farningham 862115) Courage; picturesque old coaching house, 7 bedrms for B&B, each with h & c, lounge with TV, restaurant, lunch 12.00-14.00 (13.30 Sun), dinner 19.00-21.30, both t d'hote & a la c, trad Sun lunch, Good Food Guide, bar lunches, trad ale, river-side garden
A20 s'posted Maidstone, R into village 1m

**4 P2** **Bull, Snodland** (Snodland 241033) Courage; family pub in village centre, 5 bedrms for B&B, TV in rooms, lounge, lunch 12.00-14.00 Mon-Fri, snacks other times
A228 s'posted Rochester 1½m

**5 P3 (R)** **Sir Thomas Wyatt, Allington** (Maidstone 52515) Whitbread; roadhouse type pub with restaurant, lunches Mon-Fri, dinner 19.00-22.00 (closed Sun & Mon) t d'hote & a la c
A20 s'posted Maidstone ¼m

**6 P4 (R)** **Running Horse, Sandling** Courage; popular mock Tudor thatched pub, restaurant, lunch 12.00-15.00, t d'hote & a la c every day (exc Sun) dinner 19.00-22.00 (exc Sun & Mon) a la c, substantial bar meals (exc Sun), small garden
A274 s'posted Maidstone, on L ¼m

## RESTAURANTS

**4 R1** **Bakery, West Malling** (W.M. 843247) licenced; 14th century yeoman's cottage, lunches 12.00-14.00, t d'hote & a la c, trad Sun lunch (in 3 sittings), dinner 19.00-22.00, a la c, English cooking, closed Sun evening
A228 s'posted Tonbridge, in village on L 1¼m

**6 R2** **Al Fiasco Due, Sandling** (Maidstone 63255) Licenced; private house converted to top class restaurant, lunch 12.00-14.30, t d'hote & a la c every day, dinner 19.00-22.30, t d'hote (exc weekends) & a la c, Italian & English cooking
A274 s'posted Maidstone, on R ¼m

## HOTELS

**3 H1 (R)** **Moat Hotel, Wrotham Hill** (Borough Green 882263) Freehouse; 17th century farmhouse with tithe barn alongside, now small, modern hotel, 10 rooms, h & c, some with bath, residents lounge, restaurant, lunch 12.00-14.30, a la c, trad Sun lunch, dinner 19.00-22.30 a la c, dinner dance Sat, fish speciality, bar meals daily, small garden
N on A20 on W side 1m

**3 H2 (R)** **Bull, Wrotham** (Borough Green 3092) Freehouse; old coaching house, now small hotel, 8 bedrooms each with h & c, restaurant, lunch 12.00-14.30, dinner 19.00-22.00, both t d'hote & a la c, trad Sun lunch, bar meals, trad beer, garden
A20 s'posted London, L into village 2m

**4 H3** **Swan Hotel, West Malling** (W.M. 843000) Bass; one time coaching Inn, beamed bars, modernised 12 bedrm *hotel, TV lounge, restaurant, bar meals, snacks all times open, trad Sun lunch
A228 s'posted Tonbridge, into village junction 1¼m

**End H4 (R)** **Tudor House, Bearstead** (Maidstone 37284) Freehouse; unusual old house in own grounds, 53 modern bedrms with bathrms etc, restaurant, lunch 12.00-14.30, trad lunches & a la c, dinner 18.30-22.30 (23.00 Sat) exc Sun, English & continental cooking, buffet, bars serving meals in covered courtyard, live music Fri & Sat, jazz Wed, garden
A20 s'posted Maidstone, on L ¾m

# M27. South Coast

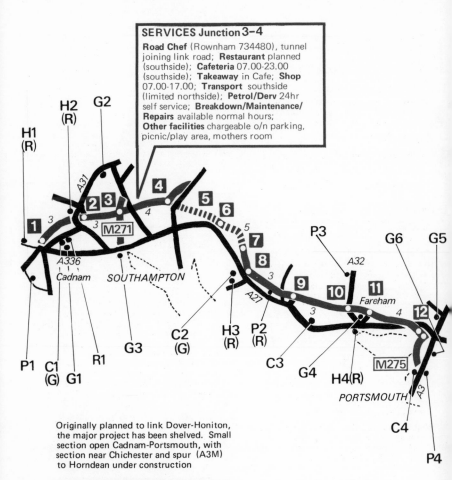

H2 (R)   G2

H1 (R)

A31

2  3

1   3

M271

A336
Cadnam

SOUTHAMPTON

4

5

6

7

8

9

10

11   Fareham

12

P3

A32

A27

3

3

4

G6   G5

M275

P1   C1 (G)   G1   R1   G3   C2 (G)   H3 (R)   P2 (R)

C3   G4   H4(R)

PORTSMOUTH   A3

C4

P4

Originally planned to link Dover-Honiton, the major project has been shelved. Small section open Cadnam-Portsmouth, with section near Chichester and spur (A3M) to Horndean under construction

**Start E** edge of **New Forest,** 1½m to Rufus Stone. **Junction 3** M271 spur to **Southampton Docks. Junction 4** eventually to link with **M3. Junction 4** to **7** not yet open, due 1980. **Junction 12** M275 spur to **Portsmouth** and **New Ferry Jetty** (no parking)

# CAFES

**End** **Courtesy Cafe & Filling Station, Cadnam**
**C1** Light meals & snacks 07.30-18.00 daily
**(G)** in summer. National, 07.30-22.00, petrol,
derv, limited spares
From r'bout at end of M, on A31
s'posted Ower, on R                              1m

**8** **Queensview Cafe & Filling Station,**
**C2** **Bursledon** 06.15-16.00 Mon-Fri, hot
**(G)** meals, snacks, special lunches. 06.00-21.00
(09.00-18.00 Sun) petrol, derv, limited
spares
A27 s'posted Eastleigh, on L                    ½m

**9** **Wimpey, Parkgate**
**C3** 09.00-18.00 (10.00-17.30 weekends),
light grills & snacks
A27 s'posted Fareham, on R                      ½m

**M275** **Ferry Terminal, Northend, Portsmouth**
**C4** Light snacks all day in ferry compound
End of M275, s'posted Ferry                     ¼m

# GARAGES

**End** **Kibbles Garage, Cadnam** (C. 2204)
**G1** 24hr bkdn (night C. 3100), **serv & rprs
normal hours
From r'bout at end of M, A336 s'posted
Totton, on L                                    1½m

**2** **Jack O'Lantern Service Station** (Ower 255)
**G2** Esso. 08.00-18.00, petrol, bkdn & rprs
normal hours
A31 s'posted Romsey, on L                       ½m

**M271** **Newmans of Redbridge** (Totton 5021)
**G3** Shell. 07.30-19.15 (09.00-18.00 Sun),
Unipart spares, *** serv & rprs, bkdn
normal hours, Leyland agent
At S end of M271, R on A36 s'posted
Totton                                          ½m

**11** **Cedar Garage, Fareham** (F. 31511)
**G4** 08.00-18.00 (closed Sun), petrol, derv,
24hr bkdn serv (night F. 80158), ***serv
& rprs normal hours, Leyland agent
At r'bout, R into town (not bypass)  1m

**12** **Cosham Filling Station, Cosham** (C.73752)
**G5** BP. 24hr petrol, AA bkdn, serv & rprs
normal hours, spares 24hr
S'posted Cosham, on L                           1m

**12** **United Services, Hilsea** (Portsmouth 70401)
**G6** Shell. 08.00-18.30 (closed Sun), petrol,
24hr bkdn, ***serv normal hours
A3 s'posted Portsmouth                          1½m

# PUBS

**End** **Trusty Servant, Minstead** (Cadnam 2137)
**P1** Whitbread; New Forest pub, 3 rooms
B&B, snacks available
Off A31 s'posted Ringwood, L to village
2½m

**8** **Old Ship, Sarisbury**
**P2** Gale; country house pub, restaurant,
**(R)** lunch 12.00-14.00, dinner 19.00-21.30,
mainly a la c, trad ale, vine-covered patio
A27 s'posted Fareham, on R          2m

**10** **Old Vine, Wickham** (W. 822079)
**P3** Ind Coope; isolated country pub, lunch
12.00-14.00, dinner 19.00-22.00 (exc
Mon), bar or restaurant, mainly grills,
garden
A32 s'posted Wickham, on R                      1m

**E End** **Admiral Drake, Northend** (Portsmouth
**P4** 60930) Whitbread; stately Victorian pub,
4 rooms B&B, light snacks, trad beer
On r'bout                                       ¼m

# RESTAURANT

**W End** **Le Chanteclere, Cadnam** (C. 3271)
**R1** Old country house, gourmet restaurant,
French cuisine, lunch 12.00-14.00,
dinner 19.00-22.00 (exc Sun & Mon),
a la c
From r'bout at W end A31 s'posted
Ower, on L                                      1m

# HOTELS

**W End** **Bell, Brook** (Cadnam 2214)
**H1** Freehouse; country ** hotel, own golf
**(R)** course for 3 day residents, 11 bedrms
(most with bath), restaurant, bkfst 07.30-
09.30, lunch 12.30-14.15, dinner 19.30-
21.30, t d'hote, trad Sun lunch, bar, trad
beer, children's play area
From r'bout at W end B3078, s'posted
Fordingbridge, to village, on R         1½m

**1** **New Forest Lodge, Ower** (O. 333)
**H2** Watneys; modern ***motel, 43 bedrms
**(R)** with bath & TV, bkfst 07.30-
09.30, lunch 12.00-14.30, dinner 19.00-
21.30, t d'hote & a la c, trad Sun lunch,
dinner dance winter Sats, trad beer,
garden
A31 s'posted Ower, on R                         ¼m

**8** **Solent Motel, Bursledon** (B. 2151)
**H3** Freehouse; modern ***motel, 52 bedrms
**(R)** with bath & TV, restaurant, bkfst
07.30-09.30, lunch 12.30-14.00, dinner
19.00-21.30, a la c, bars, garden
B3397 from r'bout, s'posted Hamble, on L
½m

**11** **Roundabout, Fareham** (F. 86411)
**H4** Freehouse; Georgian house, 23 bedrms
**(R)** with bath, TV lounge, restaurant, all
meals 07.00-23.00, t d'hote & a la c,
dinner dance/cabaret Fri & Sat, bar meals,
garden
On r'bout at Fareham Rd                         ¼m

# M40. London-Oxford

**A40** 10m of fast dual carriageway leads to start of M near **Uxbridge. Junction 1** S for **London Airport. Junction 7** end of M, dual carriageway to **Oxford.** Extension planned NW to link with Midlands Motorways

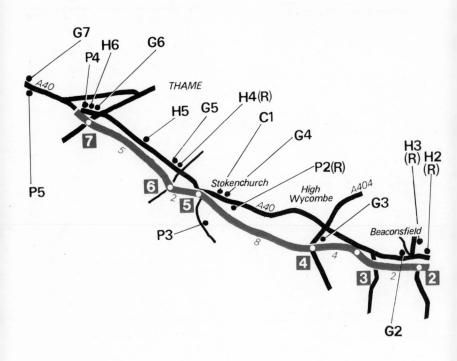

## CAFES

**5**
**C1** Roundabout Transport Cafe, **Stokenchurch** (Radnage 2131) 07.00-21.00 (13.00 Sat, closed Sun), home cooking, B&B for transport, TV
A40 s'posted Stokenchurch, at r'bout ¼m

## GARAGES

**1**
**G1** Denham Service Station, Denham (D. 2345) Esso. Petrol 24hr, AA bkdn, serv & rprs normal hours
A40 s'posted Denham, on L ½m

**2**
**G2** Old Beaconsfield Garage, Beaconsfield (B. 5616) 09.00-18.30 (exc Sun), petrol, AA serv & bkdn normal hours, limited spares, Chrysler dealer
A40 s'posted Beaconsfield, L onto A40, on L ¼m

**4** **Marlow Road Service Station, High**
**Wycombe** (HW 22888) Esso. 07.00-21.45
**G3** (09.00-21.45 Sun) petrol, derv, RAC
bkdn (night Bourne End 27065), serv &
rprs normal hours, limited spares
A404 s'posted High Wycombe, on R ¼m

**5** **Tower Garage, Stokenchurch** (Radnage
3355) Esso. Petrol 24hr prepayment,
**G4** 08.00-19.00, attendant, AA & RAC bkdn
serv. AA rprs normal hours
A40 s'posted Stokenchurch, at r'bout
¼m

**6** **Postcombe Garage, Postcombe**
(Tetsworth 222) Esso. 08.00-19.00,
**G5** petrol, derv, AA & RAC bkdn serv, serv
& rprs 08.00-19.00 daily, night emergency
serv, spares
A4009 s'posted Princes Risborough, L
on A40, on L 2m

**7** **Lantern Service Station, Milton Common**
(Gt Milton 336) Fina. 08.00-21.00 petrol
**G6** derv, RAC bkdn (night Long Grendon
208165), serv & rprs normal hours,
limited spares
To A40 s'posted Thame, L onto A40, on
R ¼m

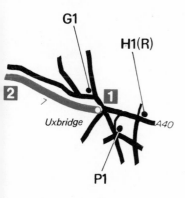

G1

H1(R)

**2**

**1**

Uxbridge

A40

P1

**W End** **Wheatley Garage, Wheatley** (W. 2227)
BP. 08.00-19.00 (exc Sun) serv & rprs
**G7** normal hours
A40 s'posted Wheatley, into village, on L
1m

## PUBS

**1** **Crown & Treaty, Uxbridge**
Whitbreads; famous old pub, modernised,
**P1** bar meals Mon-Fri, snacks other times
A413 s'posted Uxbridge, on R 2m

**5** **Kings Arms, Stokenchurch** (Radnage
516) Freehouse; creeper-covered Georgian
**P2** coaching house, 10 rms B&B, restaurant,
**(R)** lunch 12.00-14.30, dinner 19.30-22.00,
mainly grills, closed Sun, dinner dance
Sat, bar meals, garden
A40 s'posted Stokenchurch, through
town, on L 2m

**5** **Fox, Ibestone**
Whitbread; small country pub, light bar
**P3** meals & snacks, trad beer, garden
Minor road s'posted Ibestone, on L 2m

**7** **Three Pigeons, Gt Milton** (GM. 247)
Ind Coope; modern pub, bar meals,
**P4** mainly home cooking, 11.00-14.30,
18.00-22.00, live music Sat & Sun, garden
To A40 s'posted Thame, L onto A40, on R
¼m

**W End** **Bridge Hotel, Wheatley**
Freehouse; enlarged village pub, meals,
**P5** restaurant, music, garden
A40 s'posted Wheatley, into village, on L
1m

## HOTELS

**1** **Master Brewer, Hillingdon**
(Uxbridge 51199) Fullers; modern
**H1** \*\*\*hotel, 64 bedrms with bath & TV,
**(R)** foyer lounge, restaurant, bkfst 07.30-
10.30, lunch 12.30-14.30, dinner
18.30-23.00, a la c, steak bar, buffet
lunches Mon-Fri, free transport to
Heathrow Airport, garden
A40 s'posted Hillingdon, on L 2m

**2** **Bell House Hotel, Beaconsfield**
(Gerrards Cross 87211) Freehouse;
**H2** \*\*\*\*hotel, 108 bedrms with bath & TV,
**(R)** foyer lounge, bar, restaurant, bkfst
07.30-09.30, lunch 12.00-14.30, dinner
19.00-22.00, t d'hote & a la c, dinner
dance Fri & Sat, trad Sun lunch, English
& continental cooking, take-a-break
weekends, garden
To A40 s'posted Beaconsfield, R onto
A40, on R 1m

**2** **Crest Hotel, Beaconsfield** (B. 71211)
Bass; \*\*hotel, 48 bedrms (most with
**H3** bath & TV), bar, restaurant, bkfst 07.30-
**(R)** 09.30, lunch 12.00-14.00, dinner 19.00-
21.00, trad Sun lunch, t d'hote & a la c
To A40 s'posted Beaconsfield, L onto A40,
R on A355 s'posted Amersham, on L 1½m

**6** **Lambert Arms, Aston Rowant**
(Kingston Blount 51496) Freehouse;
**H4** Tudor style coaching house, 9 bedrms
**(R)** (most with bath & TV), lounge, restaurant,
lunch 12.30-14.15 t d'hote, dinner
19.00-21.45 a la c (exc Sun), bar meals,
childrens garden
A4009 s'posted Princes Risborough, L on
A40, on L ¼m

**7** **Swan, Tetsworth** (T. 281)
Freehouse; Georgian coaching house
**H5** enlarged, 22 bedrms, 6 with showers, all
with h & c, lounge, bar lunches, restaurant
evenings
To A40 s'posted Thame, R on A40 to
village, on L 2½m

**7** **Belfry Hotel, Gt Milton** (GM. 381)
Freehouse; old pub, 36 bedrms (most with
**H6** bath & TV), foyer lounge, restaurant,
bkfst 07.00-09.30, lunch 12.30-14.30,
dinner 19.00-21.30, t d'hote & a la c,
dinner dance Sat, trad Sun lunch, bar meals,
swimming pool, clay pigeon shoot, garden
To A40 s'posted Thame, L on A40, on R
¼m

# M56. North Cheshire

To link South Manchester with Ellesmere Port (A5117), Birkenhead and Wallasey (M531/M53) and A56 via Chester to North Wales

Junction **4** not yet constructed, **Junction 5** for **Manchester (Ringway) Airport.** **Junctions 8 & 13** do not yet exist **Junction 9** interchange with **M6**

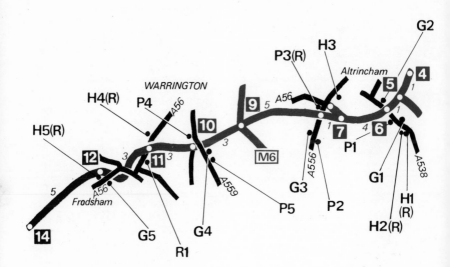

# GARAGES

**5** **G1** **Skyport Self Service, at Airport entrance** (Manchester 4378400) Gulf 24hr self serv petrol, light rprs 09.00-17.00 weekdays, RAC bkdn serv
Spur to Manchester Airport, at Airport entrance                                    ¼m

**6** **G2** **Hale Barnes Garage, Hale** (Manchester 9804116) Esso. 08.00-18.00 (exc Sun) petrol, RAC bkdn 08.30-17.30 only, serv & rprs
A538 s'posted Hale, on R               ½m

**7** **G3** **Cheshire Way Filling Station, Bucklow Hill** BP. Petrol 24hr prepayment, shop, limited spares
A556 s'posted Chester, in village on R        1½m

**10** **G4** **Ring O Bells Service Station, Lower Stretton** (Norcott Brook 551) Burmah, Petrol, AA serv & rprs
A559 s'posted Northwich, on L         ½m

**12** **G5** **Sutton Weaver Service Station** (Aston 273) Shell. 08.00-20.00 petrol, 24hr bkdn, serv & rprs 08.30-18.00 daily, car hire
To A56 s'posted Chester, L on A56, on R         1¼m

# PUBS

**6** **P1** **Romper, Ringway** (Manchester 9802390) Baddington; quaint old pub, sandwiches lunchtime Tues-Fri, trad beer
A538 s'posted Wilmslow, L to Airport        ¼m

**7** **P2** **Kilton Inn, Bucklow Hill** (BH 830420) Ex-courthouse, courtroom now restaurant (closed Sun) bar buffet lunchtime, garden
A556 s'posted Chester, on R        1½m

**7** **P3** **(R)** **Nags Head, Little Bollington** (Bucklow Hill 830323) Bass; beside motorway, bars, lunches & evening meals, restaurant open Tues-Sat for lunches, t d'hote, trad beer, garden
To A556, turn sharp L        1m

**10** **P4** **Cat and Lion, Stretton,** (Norcott Brook 229) Greenall Whitley; old pub, 2 rooms B&B, bar meals daily, trad beer, garden
A49 s'posted Warrington, on L        ½m

**10** **P5** **Birch and Bottle, Higher Whitely** Greenall Whitley; small pub, lunches daily, light evening meals, trad beer, garden
A559 s'posted Northwich, on L        1m

# RESTAURANTS

**11** **R1** **Old No. 1 Wine Bar and Restaurant, Preston Brook** (Aston 282) Freehouse; converted 18C canalside warehouse, special lunches, a la c lunch & dinner
A56 s'posted Preston Brook, L down lane in village        2m

# HOTELS

**5** **H1** **(R)** **Excelsior, Wythenshawe** (Manchester 4375811) Trust House Forte; ****hotel, 255 bedrms with bath & TV, restaurant bkfst 07.00-09.30, lunch 12.00-14.00, dinner 19.00-21.30 t d'hote & a la c, lounge, shop
Spur to Manchester Airport, in Airport        ¾m

**6** **H2** **(R)** **Valley Lodge, Oversley Ford** (Wilmslow 29201) Freehouse; continental style ***hotel, 66 bedrms with bath & TV, restaurant, bkfst 07.00-09.30, lunch, t d'hote Mon-Fri & a la c Sun, trad Sun lunch (summer barbecues if fine), dinner a la c, dinner dances (disco) Tues, Fri & Sat, over 30's (singles only) Wed
A538 s'posted Wilmslow, on L        2m

**7** **H3** **Alpine Hotel, Bowdon** (Altrincham 6191) **hotel, 15 bedrms with TV & radio, restaurant, residential licence
A56 s'posted Altrincham, R on B1560        2m

**11** **H4** **(R)** **Lord Daresbury, Daresbury** (Warrington 67331) Greenall Whitley; ***hotel, 108 bedrms with bath & TV, restaurant (with lounge), bkfst 07.30-09.30, lunch & dinners, t d'hote & a la c, in own grounds
A56 s'posted Warrington, on L        ½m

**12** **H5** **(R)** **Unicrest Hotel, Runcorn** (R. 63444) Bass; ***hotel, 141 bedrms with bath & TV, restaurant, bkfst 07.30 09.30, lunch 12.45-14.15, dinner 19.00-21.45, t d'hote & a la c, buffet, lounge bar, snacks, garden, patio
L, then L up hill on minor road        ¼m

# M61. Manchester-Preston

A short M to link Manchester and the
Midlands with Scotland and the North
via M6

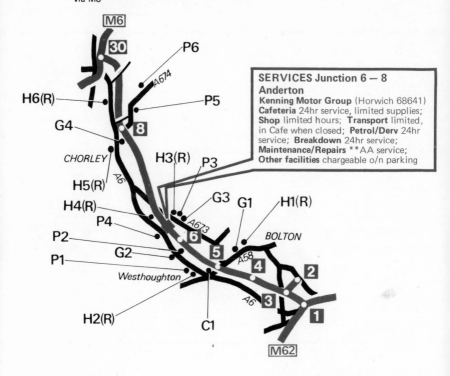

**SERVICES Junction 6 — 8
Anderton**
**Kenning Motor Group** (Horwich 68641)
**Cafeteria** 24hr service, limited supplies;
**Shop** limited hours; **Transport** limited,
in Cafe when closed; **Petrol/Derv** 24hr
service; **Breakdown** 24hr service;
**Maintenance/Repairs** **AA service;
**Other facilities** chargeable o/n parking

**Junction 1** interchange with M62.
**Junction 2/3** A666M spur. **End** interchange with M6 at Junction 30. No
southbound exit from M6

## CAFES

**5** **Travellers Rest, Westhoughton**
**C1** Licenced; B&B, meals 07.00-19.00
A58 s'posted Westhoughton, at r'bout
¼m

## GARAGES

**5** **Beaumont Service Station, Deane**
**G1** (Bolton 61726) Shell. 24hr prepayment,
serv & rprs, AA bkdn serv
A58 s'posted Bolton, on R ¾m

**6** **Shaw Motor Bodies, Fourgates,**
**G2** **Westhoughton** (WH. 2274) AA bkdn
serv
A6027 s'posted Chorley, L on A6
s'posted Westhoughton, on L 2½m

**6** **Beehive Service Station, Horwich**
**G3** Shell. 07.00-21.00, petrol, serv & rprs
normal hours
A6027 s'posted Horwich, L onto A673,
on R ¾m

**8** **Jubilee Service Station, Chorley**
**G4** (C. 2353) Chevron. 08.00-21.00 (18.00
Sun), petrol, derv, local bkdn
A6 s'posted Chorley, on L ¾m

## PUBS

**5** **Royal Oak, Westhoughton** (W.812168)
**P1** Wilsons; old world pub, bar lunches
Mon-Fri, tables outside
A58 s'posted Westhoughton, L on A6,
on L ½m

**5** **Four Gates, Westhoughton** (W.813107)
**P2** Greenall Whitley; Victorian pub,
lunches & dinners (Italian meals available),
trad beer, garden
A58 s'posted Westhoughton, R on A6,
on R ½m

**6** **Beehive, Horwich** (H. 66305)
**P3** Tetley; Victorian red brick, steak bar,
lunches & dinners, bar meals, childrens
room
A6027 s'posted Horwich, L onto A673,
on R ¼m

**6** **Happy Pig, Blackrod** (Adlington 480375)
**P4** Freehouse; pub with restaurant
A6027 s'posted Chorley, R onto A6, on L
2½m

**8** **Red Cat, Heapey** (Chorley 3966)
**P5** Matthew Brown; old fashioned one hatch
pub, bar meals, trad beer, garden
A674 s'posted Blackburn, on L ½m

**8** **Top Lock, Wheelton** (Chorley 3376)
**P6** Matthew Brown; old canalside pub,
lunches Mon-Fri, snacks evenings & weekends, garden
A674 s'posted Blackburn, L onto minor
road to canal 1m

## HOTELS

**5** **Crest Motel, Bolton** (B. 651511)
**H1** Bass; ***hotel, 100 bedrms with bath
**(R)** & TV, bars, restaurant, bkfst 07.30-
09.30, lunch 12.30-14.00, t d'hote & a
la c, dinner 18.30-21.45, a la c, bar meals,
sandwiches any time, lawns, foyers
A58 s'posted Bolton, on L ½m

**5** **Mercury Motel, Westhoughton**
**H2** (W. 813270) Small 17 room motel, TV
**(R)** lounge, grill lounge, bkfst 07.30-09.30,
lunch 12.00-14.30, dinner 18.00-22.00,
residents bar
A58 s'posted Westhoughton to r'bout,
then R on A6, on L ½m

**6** **Swallowfield, Horwich** (H. 67914)
**H3** Converted Victorian house, 8 rooms
**(R)** B&B, evening meals
A6027 s'posted Horwich, L onto A673,
on R 1½m

**6** **Georgian House, Blackrod** (Allington
**H4** 814598) Freehouse; fine old Georgian
**(R)** house, 10 bedrms with colour TV &
showers, restaurant, bkfst 07.00-09.30,
lunch 12.00-14.00, t d'hote & a la c,
dinner 19.00-22.00, a la c, dinner dances
Wed, Fri & Sat
A6027 s'posted Chorley, R onto A6,
on R 2½m

**8** **Hartwood Hall, Chorley** (C. 3241)
**H5** 10 rooms B&B, full accommodation &
**(R)** meals, restaurant, bkfst 07.30-09.30,
lunch 12.00-14.00, dinner 19.00-21.00
t d'hote & a la c
A6 s'posted Chorley, on R ¼m

**8** **Pines, Clayton le Woods** (Preston 38551)
**H6** Freehouse; **hotel, 21 bedrms with
**(R)** colour TV, restaurant, bkfst 07.00-09.30,
lunch 12.00-14.00, dinner 19.00-21.00,
t d'hote, disco dinner Fri evenings, bar
meals & snacks, squash courts
A6 s'posted Leyland, on L 2½m

# M62. Lancashire-Yorkshire

## JUNCTIONS 1 – 18 & M57

### M57 Liverpool Outer Ring Road

The Pennine M, linking the main
industrial cities of S Lancashire and
Yorkshire with Liverpool and Hull

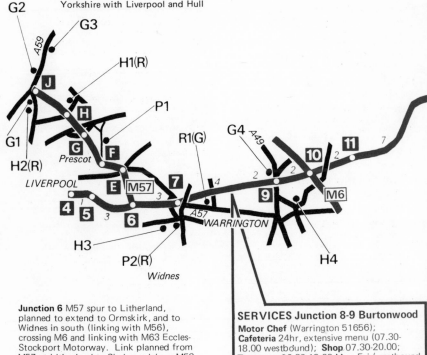

**Junction 6** M57 spur to Litherland,
planned to extend to Ormskirk, and to
Widnes in south (linking with M56),
crossing M6 and linking with M63 Eccles-
Stockport Motorway. Link planned from
M57 at Litherland to Skelmersdale as M58.
**Junction 12** M63 interchange and M602
spur to Salford. **Junction 14/15** M61
interchange. **Junction 18** M66 spur to
Heywood (to extend to Ramsbottom)
and Manchester

M57 junctions are not numbered; the AA
lettering system is used here

---

**SERVICES Junction 8-9 Burtonwood**

**Motor Chef** (Warrington 51656);
**Cafeteria** 24hr, extensive menu (07.30-
18.00 westbound); **Shop** 07.30-20.00;
**Transport** 06.30-19.00 Mon-Fri (westbound
in Cafe); **Petrol/Derv** 24hr self serv,
attendant available; **Breakdown** 24hr;
**Maintenance/Repairs** normal hours; **Other
facilities** chargeable o/n parking

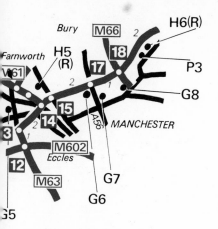

**Black Horse, Widnes** (W. 4243729)
7
P2
(R)
Greenall Whitley; old site of coaching
house, stables used as restaurant,
lunches 12.00-14.00 Mon-Fri, dinner
19.00-22.30 (exc Sun) a la c, bar lunches
A569 s'posted Widnes, at crossroads ¼m

**Gardeners Arms, Birch**
18
M66
P3
Heywood; lunches Mon-Fri, snacks
evenings & weekends
To end of M66 spur, L at r'bout to
village, on L                                                1¼m

## RESTAURANTS

**Whittle Inn, Bold Heath**
7
R1
(G)
Lunch 12.00-15.00 t d'hote & a la c,
dinner 19.00-23.00 (exc Sun) a la c,
small cocktail bar, filling station alongside (Liverpool 4242259) 07.00-22.30
(08.00-22.30 weekends), petrol, derv
A57 s'posted Warrington, on R        2m

## HOTELS

**Crest Motel, Knowsley** (Liverpool
M57
H
H1
(R)
5467531) Bass; modern ***hotel, 50
bedrms with bath & TV, restaurant,
bkfst 07.30-09.30, bar lunches only
(exc Sat), dinner 18.30-21.30 t d'hote
& a la c
A506 s'posted Kirkby, on R            1m

**Park Hotel, Netherton** (N. 5257555)
M57
J
H2
(R)
Greenall Whitley; addition to pub,
modern 54 room (most with bath & TV)
***hotel, restaurant, bkfst 07.30-09.30,
lunch 12.30-14.00, dinner 19.30-22.00
(21.00 Sun) a la c & t d'hote, bar meals,
trad Sun lunch
A59/567 s'posted Liverpool/Bootle, on R
1m

**Hill Crest, Widnes**
7
H3
Freehouse; modernised 42 bedrm hotel,
restaurant, lunches & dinners
A569 s'posted Widnes, R onto A5080
½m

**Paddington House Hotel, Paddington**
9
H4
(Warrington 816761) Freehouse; on old
road, modernised ***hotel, 36 bedrms
with bath, restaurant, bkfst 07.30-09.30,
lunch 12.00-14.00, dinner 19.00-22.00,
t d'hote & a la c, bar lunches, garden,
dinner dance most Sats
A49 s'posted Warrington, L on A50, on L
2m

**Gay Willows, Clifton** (Manchester7943761)
15
H5
(R)
Tetley; Georgian mansion, now modern
8 bedrm hotel, TV lounge, restaurant,
lunch 12.00-14.00, dinner 18.30-21.00,
t d'hote & a la c, businessman's lunch
Mon-Fri, dinner dance last Fri each month,
bar meals, garden, swings
A666 s'posted Bolton, on R          ½m

**Birch Hotel, Birch**
18
M66
H6
(R)
Private; 15 rooms B&B with bath & TV,
a la c dinner, own grounds
To end of M66 spur, L at r'bout to
village, on R                              1½m

## GARAGES

**Copple House Garage, Fazerkeley**
M57
H
G1
07.30-22.00 (10.00-20.00 Sun), serv &
rprs normal hours
A59/567 s'posted Liverpool/Bootle, on L
¼m

**Alt Filling Station, Maghull**
M57
J
G2
Jet. 07.00-22.00, petrol, derv
A59 s'posted Ormskirk, on L          ½m

**Maghull Motor Co, Maghull** (Liverpool
M57
J
G3
5264-242) AA bkdn serv (night 5319177),
rprs normal hours
A59 s'posted Ormskirk, on L          1m

**Winwick Road Garage, Longford**
9
G4
Texaco. 24hr self service petrol
A49 s'posted Newton-le-Willows, at
r'bout                                           ¼m

**Petroplus, Ellesmere** (Manchester
13
G5
7902579) Total. 07.00-23.00, petrol,
derv, bkdn & rprs normal hours
A575 s'posted Walkden, on R          ½m

**Paddock Service Station, Prestwich**
17
G6
(Manchester 7732084) Mobil. 24hr self
serv, serv & rprs 08.30-17.00 Mon-Fri
A56 s'posted Prestwich, on R          ¼m

**Grimshaw & Sons, Prestwich** (Manchester
17
G7
7738611) Petrol, serv & rprs normal
hours, AA bkdn serv, Vauxhall & Peugeot
agent
A56 s'posted Prestwich, on L          ¼m

**Stuart House Service Station, Rhode**
18
M66
G8
(Manchester 6432846) Esso. 08.00-20.00
(10.00-13.00 Sun), petrol, derv, bkdn &
rprs normal hours
To end of M66 spur, R on A576, on R
½m

## PUBS

**Derby Arms, Knowsley** (Liverpool
M57
H
P1
5463853) Tetley; large pub, steak
bar/restaurant, bar snacks
A5208 s'posted Knowsley, on R        ¾m

# M62. JUNCTIONS 19 – 26

Junction 20 627 (M) Rochdale-Oldham spur. Junction 23 Wbound entry, Ebound exit only. Junction 26 M606 spur to Bradford

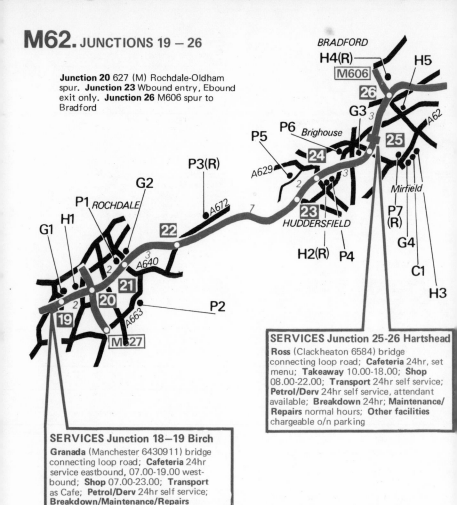

SERVICES Junction 25-26 Hartshead
**Ross** (Clackheaton 6584) bridge connecting loop road; **Cafeteria** 24hr, set menu; **Takeaway** 10.00-18.00; **Shop** 08.00-22.00; **Transport** 24hr self service; **Petrol/Derv** 24hr self service, attendant available; **Breakdown** 24hr; **Maintenance/Repairs** normal hours; **Other facilities** chargeable o/n parking

SERVICES Junction 18–19 Birch
**Granada** (Manchester 6430911) bridge connecting loop road; **Cafeteria** 24hr service eastbound, 07.00-19.00 westbound; **Shop** 07.00-23.00; **Transport** as Cafe; **Petrol/Derv** 24hr self service; **Breakdown/Maintenance/Repairs** available; **Other facilities** chargeable o/n parking, mothers room

## CAFES

**25** **Little Chef, Mirfield** (M. 492329)
**C1** Open 24hr, grills & light meals
A644 s'posted Huddersfield (east), L onto
A62, on R                                              1m

## GARAGES

**19** **Coronation Service Station, Heywood**
**G1** (H. 79767) Texaco. 07.00-22.00
(Sun 09.00-22.00), petrol, rprs normal
hours
A6046 s'posted Heywood, on L        ¼m

**21** **Milnrow Service Station** (Rochdale
**G2** 41132) Mobil. 07.15-21.30, petrol, derv,
light bkdn, serv & rprs normal hours
A640 s'posted Rochdale, R into town
                                                         ¼m

**25** **Brighouse Service Garage, Brighouse**
**G3** Shell. 07.00-19.00, petrol, derv, Leyland
agent
A644 s'posted Brighouse, on L        ½m

**25** **Three Nuns Garage, Mirfield** (M. 492391)
**G4** Shell. 07.00-19.00, petrol, derv
A644 s'posted Huddersfield (east), L onto
A62, on R                                              1m

## PUBS

**21** **Lady Barn, Milnrow** (Rochdale 42153)
**P1** Freehouse; end of dead end road, 4
rooms B&B with TV & phone, bar meals,
lunches, snacks
A640 s'posted Rochdale, L then L again
into old road                                          ¼m

**21** **Jubilee, Shaw** (S. 47540)
**P2** Watneys; Victorian roadside pub, lunches
12.00-14.00, dinners 19.00-22.30, a la c,
lunchtime buffet
A640 s'posted Oldham, R onto A663,
on L                                                  1¼m

**22** **Derby, Rishworth** (Ripponden 3674)
**P3** Freehouse; isolated moorland pub,
**(R)** restaurant, lunch 12.00-14.00, dinner
19.30-23.00 (exc Mon) t d'hote & a la c,
bar, nightly disco (exc Mon), garden
A672 s'posted Ripponden, on L      2½m

**24** **Nags Head, Ainley Top, Huddersfield**
**P4** Websters; old farmhouse, lunches, garden
A629 s'posted Huddersfield, L on A643,
on L                                                   ½m

**24** **Rock, Hollywell Green** (Elland 4329)
**P5** Freehouse; hewn out of rock, part 18C,
part new, B&B, businessmans lunch Mon-
Fri, dinner (advisable to book)
A629 s'posted Halifax, L to B6112 on R
                                                       2½m

**25** **New Tavern, Brighouse** (B. 712755)
**P6** Freehouse; restaurant, businessmans
lunches, evening meals a la c (exc Sun,
Mon & Tues), mainly grills
A644 s'posted Brighouse, into town, L
at junct then L, on L                               1m

**25** **Three Nuns, Mirfield** (M. 494233)
**P7** Tetleys; 18C coaching house, restaurant,
**(R)** steak bar, lunch 12.00-14.00, dinner
19.00-22.30 (23.30 Sat), t d'hote & a la c,
trad Sun lunch, bar meals, patio
A644 s'posted Huddersfield (east), L
onto A62, on L                                      1m

## HOTELS

**20** **Suntridge Hotel, Castleton** (Rochdale
**H1** 46504) Enlarged private house, 26
rooms (with shower & TV), dinner, B&B,
garden
A627M s'posted Oldham, R at 1st
junct, R onto A664, on R                ¼m

**24** **President, Ainley Top, Huddersfield**
**H2** (Elland 75431) Purpose built ***motel,
**(R)** 120 bedrms (with colour TV & bath),
restaurant, lunch 12.30-14.30, dinner
18.30-22.00, t d'hote & a la c, dinner
dance Sat, bar lunches, garden
A629 s'posted Huddersfield, at r'bout
on L                                                   ½m

**25** **Motel, Mirfield** (M. 492329)
**H3** Private; 10 rooms with shower, TV
lounge, meals in Little Chef alongside
A644 s'posted Huddersfield (east),
L onto A62, on R                                   1m

**26** **Novotel, Bradford** (B. 683683)
**M606** Freehouse; modern, 136 bedrms (with
**H4** TV & bath) restaurant, meals 06.30-
**(R)** 23.30, lunch 11.30-15.00, dinner 18.30-
21.30, t d'hote & a la c, swimming pool,
barbecue (weather permitting), garden
M606 spur, R at end of M, on R     ¼m

**26** **Prospect Hall, Cleckheaton** (C. 3012)
**H5** Freehouse; converted private house,
bars, restaurant
A638 s'posted Dewsbury, on L        1m

# M62. JUNCTIONS 27–34

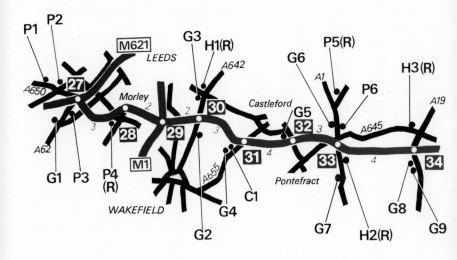

**Junction 27** M621 spur to Leeds.
**Junction 29** M1 interchange. **Junction 33**
A1(M) planned to link here, joining M18
south to M1

## CAFES

**31**
**C1** Sandpiper, Normanton (Wakefield 892112) Transport cafe, meals & snacks, 08.00-14.00 (exc Sun), 12 rooms B&B
A655 s'posted Normanton, on R ¼m

## GARAGES

**27**
**G1** Paradise Service Station, Birstall
Texaco. Petrol, derv, heavy bkdn available
A62 s'posted Birstall, on R ¾m

**30**
**G2** Cinema Garage, Stanley (Wakefield 826242) Thrust; 08.00-18.30, petrol, bkdn, serv & rprs normal hours
A642 s'posted Wakefield, on L ¾m

**30**
**G3** Gibbs Garage, Oulton (O. 74473)
Shell. 07.00-18.00 (exc Sun), petrol, derv, serv & rprs normal hours
A642 s'posted Rothwell, on L ¾m

**31**
**G4** Willow Bridge Motors, Normanton
08.00-19.00, petrol, serv & rprs
A655 s'posted Normanton, on R 1½m

**32**
**G5** Simpsons Garage, Castleford
Shell. 24hr prepayment petrol (attendant 08.00-20.00), serv & rprs, Leyland agent
A639 s'posted Castleford, on L ½m

**33**
**G6** Ferrybridge Service Station, Ferrybridge (Knottingley 85297) Esso. 24hr petrol, derv, AA recov, serv & rprs
A1 (North) on L ¼m

**33**
**G7** Knottingley Service Station, Ferrybridge (Knottingley 2484) Burmah. 24hr petrol, 24hr bkdn, serv & rprs
A1 s'posted Doncaster, on L ½m

**34**
**G8** Station Garage, Whitley Bridge
(W.B. 661668) Shell. 07.00-19.00 (09.00-14.00 Sun) petrol, derv, AA bkdn, serv & rprs normal hours
A19 s'posted Doncaster, on R ¼m

**34**
**G9** Whitley Garage, Whitley (W.B. 661496)
Burmah. 08.00-20.00, petrol only, light bkdn, serv & rprs normal hours
A19 s'posted Doncaster, on L ¾m

## PUBS

**27**
**P1** Kings Arms, Drighlington
Bass; stone-built pub, restaurant, bar meals, trad Sun lunch
A650 s'posted Bradford, on R 2m

**27**
**P2** Spotted Cow, Drighlington (D. 852558)
John Smith; old smithy-cum-small-holding, now character pub, lunches 12.00-14.00 (exc Sun), bar snacks, buffet, salads, evenings & weekends, patio
A650 s'posted Bradford, R onto A58, on L 2m

**27**
**P3** Pheasant, Birstall (Batley 473022)
Whitbread; small wayside pub, lunches Mon-Fri, snacks other times, garden
A62 s'posted Birstall ¾m

**28**
**P4**
**(R)** New White Bear, Tingley (Morley 532768)
Schooner Inns, popular steak house
A653 s'posted Dewsbury ¼m

**33**
**P5**
**(R)** Brotherton Fox, Brotherton
Bass; red brick pub, recently modernised, residential, restaurant, bar meals
A1 (North), then R onto A162 2m

**33**
**P6** Golden Lion, Ferry Bridge (Knottingley 82132) Tetley; busy riverside pub, 7 rooms B&B, evening meal available, bar lunches, garden
A1 (North), R in Ferry Bridge, L at junct, on R 1m

## HOTELS

**30**
**H1**
**(R)** Crest Hotel, Oulton (Leeds 826201)
Bass; ***hotel, 40 bedrm (with TV & bath), lounges, restaurant, bkfst 07.00-09.30, lunch 12.00-14.30, dinner 19.00-21.30, t d'hote & a la c, set Sun lunch, bars, bar meals, garden
A642 s'posted Rothwell, at junct A639 ¾m

**33**
**H2**
**(R)** Darrington Hotel, Darrington (Pontefract 71458) Scottish & Newcastle; large main road pub, 14 bedrms (with TV & showers), restaurant, bkfst 07.30-09.00 lunch 12.00-14.00, dinner 19.00-21.00 (exc Sun) both t d'hote & a la c, bar meals
A1 s'posted Doncaster, on R 2m

**34**
**H3**
**(R)** Main Motor Inn, Eggborough, Whitley Bridge (W.B. 661395) Freehouse; **hotel, 15 bedrms (with colour TV & bath), restaurant, bkfst 07.00-09.00, lunch 12.00-14.00, dinner 18.30-22.00 t d'hote & a la c, bar meals, non-residents welcome
A19 s'posted Selby, L on A645, on R 1m

# M62. JUNCTIONS 35-38

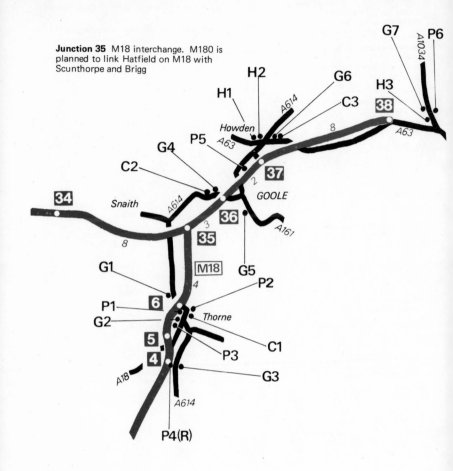

**Junction 35** M18 interchange. M180 is planned to link Hatfield on M18 with Scunthorpe and Brigg

# CAFES

**[M18] [6] C1 White House Transport Cafe, Thorne**
07.30-18.00 (07.30-15.00 Sat, 10.00-
16.00 Sun), table licence
A614 s'posted Thorne, on R          1m

**[36] C2 Woodside Transport Cafe, Rawcliffe**
Goole 83478) Family cafe, home
cooking, 06.30-18.00 Mon-Fri, all
meals & snacks, cakes & pies, o/n
parking, caravan park
A614 s'posted Rawcliffe, on R      ½m

**[37] C3 Penny Farthing, Howden** (H.30824)
07.00-18.00, grills & snacks all day
A63 to centre of Howden, R onto A63,
on R                                1m

# GARAGES

**[M18] [6] G1 Selby Road Garage, Thorne**
BP. 08.00-20.00, petrol, derv, serv &
rprs normal hours, Renault agent
A614 s'posted Goole, on R          ¼m

**[M18] [6] G2 Adams Garage, Thorne** (T. 812345)
Esso. 08.00-20.30 (09.00-20.00 Sun),
petrol, derv, serv & rprs, bkdn normal
hours, Leyland agent
A614 s'posted Thorne, R in village   ¼m

**[M18] [4] G3 Green Tree Garage, Hatfield Woodhouse**
(Doncaster 840488) Esso. 08.00-20.00
(09.00-20.00 Sun), AA bkdn serv, serv &
rprs normal hours
A18 s'posted Scunthorpe, R onto A614
s'posted Bawtry, on L              ¾m

**[36] G4 Glews Garage, Boothferry** (Goole 2357)
Texaco. 07.30-22.00 (10.00-22.00 Sun),
24hr prepayment, 24hr bkdn (Goole 3570
after 17.00), serv & rprs normal hours, get
you home service, Chrysler agent
A614 s'posted Rawcliffe, on L      ¼m

**[36] G5 Parish, Goole** (G. 3592)
AA bkdn (night G. 3299), Leyland agent
A614 s'posted Goole, R on A161 to
village                            1½m

**[37] G6 Howden Services, Howden**
Shell. 08.00-20.00 petrol, serv, serv &
bkdn normal hours
To centre of Howden, L onto A63, on R
1m

**[38] G7 Gibsons Service Station, North Cave**
(N.C. 2800) Shell. 08.00-20.00 petrol,
derv, serv & rprs normal hours, light
bkdn
A63 s'posted Kingston, L into village, L
on L                               2½m

# PUBS

**[M18] [6] P1 Belmont Hotel, Thorne** (T. 812320)
Freehouse; red brick, 26 rooms B&B
(some with bath), TV lounge, lunches,
dinners
A614 s'posted Thorne, in village, on R
¾m

**[M18] [6] P2 White Hart, Thorne, Darley** (T. 813104)
Small town pub, 4 rooms B&B, trad Sun
lunch, snacks lunchtime & evenings
during week, lunches in winter
A614 s'posted Thorne, in village centre,
on L                               ¾m

**[M18] [6] P3 Punch Bowl Inn, Thorne**
Freehouse; private house in own
grounds, lunches daily (exc Wed)
A614 s'posted Thorne, R in village, on R
½m

**[M18] [4] P4 (R) Green Tree, Hatfield Woodhouse, Darley**
(Doncaster 840305) Old farmhouse;
restaurant, lunch 12.00-14.00, dinner
19.00-22.30 (exc Mon), t d'hote & a la c,
dinner dance Sat, bar meals & snacks,
garden
A18 s'posted Scunthorpe, R onto A614
s'posted Bawtry, on L              ½m

**[37] P5 Ferry Boat Inn, Booth Ferry, Howden**
(H.30300) Freehouse; ex-ferrymans house
by River Ouse, 6 rooms B&B, bar lunches
daily, organ music Tues & Thurs evenings
To Howden, L onto A614, on L       1m

**[38] P6 Fox & Coney, South Cave** (North Cave
2275) Camerons; quiet old village pub,
lunch (exc Mon), snacks daily, trad beer
A63 s'posted Kingston, L into village, on R
2½m

# HOTELS

**[37] H1 Bowmans Hotel, Howden** (H. 30805)
Freehouse; old coaching house,
modernised, 13 bedrms (with TV & bath),
restaurant, residents lounge
To centre of Howden                 1m

**[37] H2 Wellington Hotel, Howden** (H. 30258)
Freehouse; old post house, 10 bedrms
B&B, evening meals available, family
atmosphere, bar lunches daily, organ music
Tues & Thurs
R on A614, L to centre of Howden    1m

**[38] H3 Castle Hotel, South Cave**
Freehouse; converted castle in own
grounds, 13 bedrms, restaurant, bars
A63 s'posted Kingston, L s'posted South
Cave, L at crossing, on R          2½m

# M73. Maryville Link Road
# M74. Blackwood - Glasgow

M74 links A74 Carlisle-Glasgow to outskirts of Glasgow, continuing as M73 bypassing Glasgow to the east, eventually linking to M80 via A80 dual carriageway, and to M9 via M876

**All junction numbers refer to M74 unless preceded by M73**

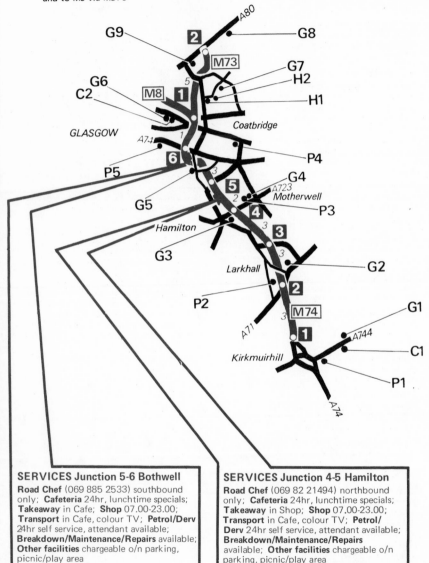

**SERVICES Junction 5-6 Bothwell**
**Road Chef** (069 885 2533) southbound only; **Cafeteria** 24hr, lunchtime specials; **Takeaway** in Cafe; **Shop** 07.00-23.00; **Transport** in Cafe, colour TV; **Petrol/Derv** 24hr self service, attendant available; **Breakdown/Maintenance/Repairs** available; **Other facilities** chargeable o/n parking, picnic/play area

**SERVICES Junction 4-5 Hamilton**
**Road Chef** (069 82 21494) northbound only; **Cafeteria** 24hr, lunchtime specials; **Takeaway** in Shop; **Shop** 07.00-23.00; **Transport** in Cafe, colour TV; **Petrol/Derv** 24hr self service, attendant available; **Breakdown/Maintenance/Repairs** available; **Other facilities** chargeable o/n parking, picnic/play area

## CAFES

**1** **Transport Cafe, Kirkmuirhill, Blackwood**
**C1** (Lesmahagow 3260), small house, lorry park opposite, 06.00-23.00 daily, home cooking, TV in cafe, accommodation
A74 s'posted Carlisle, A744 s'posted Lanark, on R                                    1m

M73 **Little Chef Grill, Coatbridge** (Glasgow
**1** 771-3245) 24hr service, grills, light meals
**C2** A8 s'posted Glasgow, on R                    1½m

## GARAGES

**1** **Kirkmuir Service Station, Kirkmuirhill, Blackwood** (Lesmahagow 3307), Texaco.
**G1** 07.00-21.00 petrol, derv, 24hr AA bkdn serv, serv & rprs normal hours
A74 s'posted Carlisle, A744 s'posted Lanark, on L                                   1m

**2** **Shawsburn Garage, Shawsburn** (Larkhall
**G2** 885205) 09.00-21.00, petrol, derv, rprs by appointment only
A71 s'posted Edinburgh                         2m

**4** **Andrew Owen, Hamilton**
**G3** BP. Petrol, serv normal hours, Toyota agent
A723 s'posted Hamilton, on L        ¼m

**4** **Braedale Garage, Motherwell**
**G4** Mobil. 08.00-21.00 petrol, rprs normal hours
A723 s'posted Motherwell, on L       ½m

**6** **Blue Diamond, Uddingston** (U. 818806)
**G5** AA bkdn, **serv & rprs
A74 s'posted Carlisle, on L            1½m

M73 **Hillcrest Service Station, Coatbridge**
**1** Esso. Self serv petrol 08.00-22.00
**G6** (09.00-21.00 weekends), bkdn normal hours with emergency call out, serv & rprs normal hours
A8 s'posted Glasgow, on R              1½m

M73 **Ronald Street Garage, Coatbridge**
**2** (C. 22030) Petrol. 24hr bkdn serv
**G7** A8 s'posted Glasgow, R onto A89 s'posted Coatbridge, L on A752, R into Coatbridge
2m

M73 **Mill Motors, Mollinsburn** (Glenboig
**2** 872347) Petrol, serv & rprs, AA bkdn
**G8** A80 s'posted Stirling, on R          ½m

M73 **Robin Hood Motors, Muirhead** (Glasgow
**2** 7791716) Petrol, serv & rprs normal
**G9** hours, AA bkdn
A80 s'posted Glasgow, on L            ¾m

## PUBS

**1** **Southfield Hotel, Blackwood**
**P1** (Lesmahagow 2233) Scottish & Newcastle; small roadside pub, 4 rooms B&B
A74 s'posted Carlisle, A744 s'posted Lanark, on R                                   ¼m

**2** **Shorelands Roadhouse, Larkhall**
**P2** (Stonehouse 791294) Freehouse; 6 rooms B&B, lunches & evening meals
A71 s'posted Kilmarnock, R onto B7068
¼m

**4** **Electric Bar, Motherwell**
**P3** Tennants; modern pub, light lunches, evening meals
A723 s'posted Motherwell, on R, in side road                                        ¼m

**5** **Hallonrigg, Bellshill** (Glasgow 2393488)
**P4** Scottish & Newcastle; small town pub, 8 rooms B&B
A725 s'posted Belshill, through Belshill to A8 junction                             2¼m

**6** **Old Mail Coach and Ostlers Halt, Broom-house** (Glasgow 7711569) Scottish &
**P5** Newcastle; modernised coaching house, steak-house, fixed price grills, 11.00-15.00 & 17.00-23.00 daily (exc Sun), limited Sun service, live music (exc Sun), snacks
A74 s'posted Glasgow, on L            ½m

## HOTELS

M73 **Coatbridge Hotel, Coatbridge** (C. 24392)
**1** Scottish & Newcastle; modern ***hotel, 22 bedrms (bath & TV), restaurant,
**H1** public bars
A8 s'posted Glasgow, R onto A89 s'posted Coatbridge, L on A752, on R         1¾m

M73 **Georgian, Lefroy Street, Coatbridge**
**1** (C. 24392) Scottish & Newcastle; 9 rooms B&B
**H2** A8 s'posted Glasgow, R onto A89 s'posted Coatbridge, L on A752, R into Coatbridge, on R                                           1¾m

# M90. Inverkeithing-Perth

Mainly dual carriageway. Not yet completed between Glenfarg and Bridge of Earn (temporary end of M at Glenfarg numbered 8A for reference purposes). M85 spur to River Tay not yet completed. No official M services; Forth Bridge Services 2½m from Junction 1, unofficial service area at Junction 6

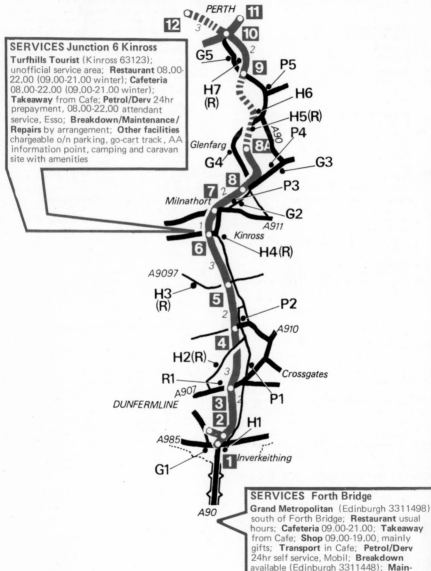

**SERVICES Junction 6 Kinross**
**Turfhills Tourist** (Kinross 63123); unofficial service area; **Restaurant** 08.00-22.00 (09.00-21.00 winter); **Cafeteria** 08.00-22.00 (09.00-21.00 winter); **Takeaway** from Cafe; **Petrol/Derv** 24hr prepayment, 08.00-22.00 attendant service, Esso; **Breakdown/Maintenance/Repairs** by arrangement; **Other facilities** chargeable o/n parking, go-cart track, AA information point, camping and caravan site with amenities

PERTH

Glenfarg

Milnathort

Kinross

Crossgates

DUNFERMLINE

Inverkeithing

**SERVICES  Forth Bridge**
**Grand Metropolitan** (Edinburgh 3311498) south of Forth Bridge; **Restaurant** usual hours; **Cafeteria** 09.00-21.00; **Takeaway** from Cafe; **Shop** 09.00-19.00, mainly gifts; **Transport** in Cafe; **Petrol/Derv** 24hr self service, Mobil; **Breakdown** available (Edinburgh 3311448); **Maintenance/Repairs** limited, **Other facilities** o/n parking, licensed motel at rear

# GARAGES

**2** **Camdean Service Station, Rosyth**
**G1** (Inverkeithing 2085) Petrol, AA bkdn, serv & rprs normal hours
M90 spur, L onto A823, at A985 junct
1¾m

**7** **Stuart and Smart, Milnathort** (Kinross
**G2** 62423) Esso. 08.00-20.00 (10.00-20.00 Sun), petrol, derv, AA bkdn, gen rprs
A91 s'posted Milnathort, L onto B996, on R
½m

**8** **Gateside Garage, Gateside** (Strathmiglo
**G3** 410) BP. 07.00-19.00, petrol, derv, bkdn, gen rprs
A91 s'posted Strathmiglo, on R
2½m

**8A** **Glenfarg Garage, Glenfarg** (G. 324)
**G4** Shell. 08.00-20.30, petrol, derv, 24hr bkdn, rprs & serv normal hours
A90 s'posted Glenfarg, on R
1m

**9** **Bridge Motors, Bridge of Earn** (BoE.2256)
**G5** Esso. 08.00-20.00 petrol (10.00-20.00 Sun), 24hr bkdn, serv & rprs normal hours
A90 s'posted Bridge of Earn, on L
½m

# PUBS

**3** **White Elephant, Hill of Beath**
**P1** (Cowdenbeath 510665) Freehouse; country pub; 2 modern rooms B&B, dinner available, bar meals & snacks, live entertainment (exc Mon)
A907 s'posted Cowdenbeath, L onto A910, at A917 junct
¾m

**4** **Oakfield Hotel, Kelty** (K. 830247)
**P2** Lorrimers; country pub in coal mining area, 5 rooms B&B, bar lunches, high teas, supper dance Sat, entertainment during week
A909 s'posted Cowdenbeath, on R
¾m

**7** **Thistle, Milnathort** (Kinross 63222)
**P3** Freehouse; small town pub, 6 rooms B&B, restaurant
A91 s'posted Milnathort, L onto B996, on R
½m

**8** **Edenshead Arms, Gateshead** (Strathmiglo
**P4** 439) Freehouse; small country pub, bar lunches weekdays, snacks available other times, garden
A91 s'posted Strathmiglo, on L
2m

**9** **Baiglie Inn, Aberargie** (Abernethy 332)
**P5** Lorrimers; isolated old pub, 2 rooms B&B, bar lunches, sandwiches & pies in evening
A90 s'posted Abernethy, on R
1m

# RESTAURANTS

**3** **Armandos Hideaway, Halbeath**
**R1** (Dunfermline 25474) Lunch 12.30-14.30, dinner 18.30-22.00, t d'hote & a la c, 1-course lunch available, closed Sun
A907 s'posted Dunfermline, R immed onto minor road, on L
¾m

# HOTELS

**1** **Queens, Inverkeithing** (I. 3075)
**H1** Small country town hotel, 13 rooms B&B, bar
A92 s'posted Kircaldy. R onto A981, on L
2m

**3** **Halfway House Hotel, Kingseat**
**H2** (Dunfermline 31661) Freehouse; ex
**(R)** coaching house, ***hotel, 12 bedrms with TV & bath, lounge, restaurant, bkfst 07.30-22.30, lunch 12.00-14.30, dinner 19.30-22.00, a la c, bar meals dinner dance Fri & Sat, 4 bars, entertainment & folk music Tues & Thurs
A907 s'posted Dunfermline, R on B912, on L in village
1m

**5** **Nivingston House, Cleish** (Cleish Hill 216)
**H3** Freehouse; private house in own grounds,
**(R)** 4 rooms B&B or full board, TV lounge, bar snacks, restaurant, lunch 12.00-14.00 (buffet table summer, a la c winter), dinner, t d'hote, Chef of Scotland award 1977, gourmet cooking, fishing & golf nearby
A9097 s'posted Crook of Devon, into Cleish, on L
1m

**6** **Green Hotel, Kinross** (K. 63467)
**H4** Freehouse; 18C coaching house,
**(R)** ***hotel, 50 bedrms (most with bath), TV lounge, restaurant, dinner t d'hote & a la c, buffet 11.00 until late evening, tennis, own fishing & golf course, swimming, squash, sauna, curling, gardens
A977 s'posted Kinross, on R
1m

**8A** **Bein Inn Hotel, Glenfarg** (G. 216)
**H5** Freehouse; character coaching house, **
**(R)** hotel, 10 bedrms (most with bath), restaurant, bkfst 08.00-09.30, full meals 10.00-18.00 hot or cold, dinner 19.00 -21.00, t d'hote, fishing & golf
A90 s'posted Perth, on R
1m

**8A** **Glenfarg Lodge, Glenfarg** (Abernethy 208)
**H6** Private; ex 11C chapel, now family hotel, 5 rooms B&B, evening meals available
A90 s'posted Perth, on L
2½m

**9** **Moncrieffe Arms Hotel, Bridge of Earn**
**H7** (BofE 2216) Freehouse; 17C inn, **hotel
**(R)** in own grounds, 10 bedrms (some with bath), restaurant, bkfst 08.00-09.30, lunch 12.15- 14.00, dinner 19.00-21.00, t d'hote & a la c, bar lunches, evening snacks, family cooking, garden
A90 s'posted Bridge of Earn, on R
½m

# A1(M) Durham

## 194 M EXTENSION TO TYNE TUNNEL AND SOUTH SHIELDS

**SERVICES Junction I–J
Washington/Birtley**

**Granada** (Chester le Street 403436) connecting bridge, loop road joining; **Cafeteria** 24hr service, daily lunch choice; **Shop** 07.00-23.00; **Petrol/Derv** 24hr self serve, attendant available; **Other facilities** chargeable o/n parking, mothers room, daily postal collections

Junction numbers have not yet been officially allocated; for identification they are lettered A-J, continued on 194M with K-M

P6(R)

G7

M

L  A184

2

J  1

K

1

I  H4(R)

1

H

Chèster-le-Street

G6

A1  6

G

G5

P5

DURHAM

5

H3 (R)

F

G4

A177

H2(R)

6

E

A689

Sedgefield  P4

A1  5

P3

D

G3

3

C  P2

6

DARLINGTON

B

4

A

G2

G1

H1(R)

A1

P1(R)

Scotch Corner

C2

C1

## CAFES

**A**
**C1** **Little Chef, Skeeby** (S. 3768)
08.00-21.00, snacks & grills
A1 s'posted Catterick, S of Scotch
Corner                                                    1m

**A**
**C2** **Transport Cafe, Scotch Corner**
07.00-19.00 Mon-Fri, accommodation
A1 s'posted Catterick, at Scotch Corner
                                                          ¾m

## GARAGES

**A**
**G1** **Highborough Moor Garage, Skeeby**
(Richmond 2764) Shell. Petrol, derv,
24hr, bkdn 24hr (night R.811344)
A1 s'posted Catterick, S of Scotch Corner
                                                          1m

**A**
**G2** **Scotch Corner Filling Station, Scotch
Corner** Esso. Petrol, derv, 24hr
A1 s'posted Catterick, at Scotch Corner
                                                          1¼m

**D**
**G3** **Kelton Garage, Aycliffe** (A. 2150)
08.00-20.00 (10.00-14.00 Sat),
petrol, derv, AA bkdn
A167 s'posted Darlington, on R      ½m

**F**
**G4** **Clarence Service, Coxhoe** (C. 770500)
24hr bkdn, serv, major rprs
A177 s'posted Peterlee, on R        ¼m

**G**
**G5** **Ramside Motors, Carrville** (Durham
62607) Shell. 08.00-21.00, bkdn, serv &
rprs normal hours
A690 s'posted Sunderland, on R      ¼m

**H**
**G6** **Motor Centre, Chester le Street**
(CS. 882266) Texaco. 07.00-24.00
(09.00-24.00 Sun), 24hr bkdn (night
Stanley 35656), serv normal hours
A167 s'posted Chester le Street, on R
                                                          1m

**M**
**G7** **Wardle Service Station, Wardle** (Felling
692433), Esso. 08.00-21.00 (10.00 Sun),
petrol, derv, bkdn & rprs normal hours
A184 s'posted Gateshead, on L       1m

## PUBS

**A**
**P1**
**(R)** **Black Bull, Molton** (Barton 289)
Freehouse; unassuming but fascinating,
3 restaurants (one in an old Pullman
coach in garden, one in conservatory,
one panelled room for fish specialities
incl lobster fresh from tank), lunch 12.00-
14.00, dinner 19.00-20.00, set menu in
each restaurant, bar lunches & snacks
A1 s'posted Catterick, S of Scotch Corner,
E to village, on R                  2½m

**D**
**P2** **White Horse, Harrowgate Village**
(Darlington 55854) Camerons; bar lunches,
carvery, limited a la c lunches 12.00-
14.00, dinners 19.00-23.00 in restaurant
(exc Sun), sandpit for children
A167 s'posted Darlington, on R      1½m

**E**
**P3** **Hardwick Arms, Sedgfield** (S. 20218)
Scottish & Newcastle; old coaching
house in racecourse village, 7 rooms B&B,
evening meal available
A689 s'posted Teeside, in village, on L
                                                          2½m

**E**
**P4** **Nags Head, Sedgfield** (S. 20234)
Bass, 17C village pub, lunchtime bar
meals, evening grills 19.00-21.30
A689 s'posted Teeside, in village, on L
                                                          2½m

**G**
**P5** **Grange, Carrville** (Durham 2082)
Camerons; village pub, dining room,
lunches (exc Mon), trad Sun lunch, bar
meals, evening grills 19.00-21.30 (exc Mon)
A690 s'posted Sunderland, R to village,
on R                                ¼m

**M**
**P6**
**(R)** **White Hart, Felling** (Newcastle 698121)
Scottish & Newcastle; bar lunches,
restaurant, lunch a la c & t d'hote (exc
Sun), dinner 19.00-22.30 daily (exc Mon)
with music hall, French & English
cuisine, booking essential
A184 s'posted Sunderland, on R      ¼m

## HOTELS

**A**
**H1**
**(R)** **Scotch Corner Hotel, Scotch Corner**
(Richmond 2943) Freehouse; on site of
coaching inn, *** hotel, 50 bedrms (bath
& TV in most), lounge, restaurant, bkfst
07.30-10.00, lunch 12.00-14.00, dinner
19.00-23.00, t d'hote & a la c, dinner dance
Sat, grill room, teas 15.00-18.00, garden
A1 s'posted Catterick, W on A66 s'posted
Bowes, on L                         ¼m

**E**
**H2**
**(R)** **Eden Arms Hotel, Rushyford** (R. 541)
Vaux; 44 bedrms (most with TV & bath),
B&B, restaurant, bkfst 07.30-09.30, lunch
12.30-14.15 (exc Sat & Sun), summer
buffet 12.00-14.00, t d'hote & a la c,
dinner dance Sat Sept-May, bar meals,
trad Sun lunch, garden
A689 s'posted Bishop Auckland, on L
                                                          2m

**F**
**H3**
**(R)** **Bowburn Hall Hotel, Bowburn**
(Coxhoe 777300) Freehouse; converted
colliery managers house, 20 bedrms (with
TV & bath), restaurant, lunches mainly in
bar lounge, dinners (19.00-23.30, a la c
& t d'hote, tennis court, garden
A177 s'posted Durham, 1st R, then L,
on L                                ¾m

**I**
**H4**
**(R)** **Post House, Washington** (W. 462264)
Trust House Forte; purpose built hotel,
144 bedrms with TV & bath (used on
President Carter's 1977 visit as American
Embassy), restaurant, bkfst 07.30-10.00,
buttery open for all meals until 22.30,
lunch 12.30-14.00, dinner 19.00-23.00,
t d'hote & a la c, dinner dance Fri & Sat
in winter, bar lunches Mon-Fri, garden,
special weekend rates
A1231 s'posted Washington, L on minor
road, overlooking motorway          ¼m